THE
PRACTICAL
QUIZ BOOK

by

John Barton

PAPERFRONTS

Typeset in 10/11pt Times by
County Typesetters, Margate, Kent.

Printed and bound in Great Britain by
Cox & Wyman Ltd., Reading.

The *Paperfronts* series and the *Right Way* series are both published by Elliot Right Way Books, Brighton Road, Lower Kingswood, Tadworth, Surrey, KT20 6TD, U.K.

To: Max and Alison

In the same series

- All British Quiz Book
- Progressive Brain-Teasing Quizzes
- Boost Your Vocabulary

Popular Quiz Book

Family Fun Quiz Book

Quick Question Quiz Book

General Knowledge Quiz Book

Standard Quiz Book

- By the same author

Uniform with this book

CONTENTS

INTRODUCTION

This is a *really different* quiz book. Why? Because it is *useful*. Most quiz books contain questions like 'What was the date of the battle of Marathon?' or 'What was Franklin Roosevelt's middle name?' which however interesting they may be are of no practical everyday use.

Most of the questions and answers in this quiz book, however, are guaranteed to be of use in your business, domestic or social life, on holiday, in the home, on the road, at the office, or in the garden.

Some of them will save you money, others will save you time and effort, and one or two might even save your life! They are all *useful* pieces of knowledge and interesting too.

I am once again indebted to too many works of reference for individual mention, except for the inestimable *Oxford English Dictionary*. Also my thanks to my wife for reading the manuscript and helping with several of the sections. For any mistakes I am entirely to blame and the publishers and I would be grateful if they were brought to our notice.

John Barton

ABBREVIATIONS

1. These bodies are often in the news. What are they?
   (a) OPEC; (b) CND; (c) EC; (d) MCC.

2. The letters ISBN (with a number) appear in most published books. What do they stand for?

3. What are the abbreviations RSVP and PS, sometimes seen at the end of a letter?

4. What are the full names of these companies? (a) ICI; (b) GEC; (c) IBM; (d) P and O.

5. My ETA is 1100 hours GMT and I have an appointment at the LSE to discuss the IMF with an MP. What do the abbreviations mean?

6. SALT (not the condiment) is important to European countries. Why?

7. What are these decorations?
   (a) DSO; (b) VC;   (c) GC; (d) DFC.

8. You will often see a TIR plate on an HGV. Explain.

9. What is UCCA and why is it interested in the GCSE?

10. Which of these metallic elements is normally a liquid?
    Cu   Hg   Au   Ra   Ag

11. What are these books? (a) DNB; (b) OED.

12. What are these academic honours?
    (a) DD; (b) BCL.

ABBREVIATIONS

1. (*a*) Organization of Petroleum Exporting Countries; (*b*) Campaign for Nuclear Disarmament; (*c*) European Community; (*d*) Marylebone Cricket Club.

2. International Standard Book Number.

3. *Répondez s'il vous plaît* and postscript.

4. (*a*) Imperial Chemical Industries;
   (*b*) General Electric Company;
   (*c*) International Business Machines;
   (*d*) Peninsular and Oriental Steamship Company.

5. ETA = estimated time of arrival; GMT = Greenwich Mean Time; LSE = London School of Economics; IMF = International Monetary Fund; MP = Member of Parliament.

6. SALT is the Strategic Arms Limitation Treaty.

7. (*a*) Distinguished Service Order; (*b*) Victoria Cross; (*c*) George Cross; (*d*) Distinguished Flying Cross.

8. TIR = *Transport International Routier* (International Road Transport); HGV = heavy goods vehicle.

9. UCCA = Universities Central Council on Admissions; GCSE = General Certificate of Secondary Education.

10. Hg (mercury).

11. (*a*) Dictionary of National Biography; (*b*) Oxford English Dictionary.

12. (*a*) Doctor of Divinity; (*b*) Bachelor of Civil Law.

2. Questions

Your BODY

1. What is the normal pulse-rate and temperature of the average human body?

2. How many bones are there in the adult human body?
   152   180   206   231   250

3. There are four blood groups: A, B, AB and O. (*a*) Which group can receive blood from any other group? (*b*) Which group can give blood to any other group?

4. (*a*) Is the air we breathe in mostly oxygen, nitrogen or carbon dioxide? (*b*) How about the air we breathe out?

5. What do these glands produce? (*a*) pancreas; (*b*) thyroid.

6. How many breaths does a person take per minute?

7. (*a*) How much blood does the average person carry? (*b*) What is the name for the liquid part of the blood and what percentage of water does it contain?

8. How many teeth should a normal adult have? Name the four types of tooth.

9. What are the common names for these bones?
   (*a*) patella; (*b*) femur; (*c*) clavicle; (*d*) scapula.

10. Where are these bones? (*a*) fibula; (*b*) carpals; (*c*) humerus; (*d*) radius.

11. Where is most of the food that we eat absorbed into the bloodstream?

12. Is it harmful to drink too much or too little water?

Your BODY

1. Pulse: 72 beats per minute.
   Temperature: 98.6 °Fahrenheit.

2. 206.

3. (*a*) AB; (*b*) O.

4. (*a*) nitrogen 78%, oxygen 21%;
   (*b*) nitrogen 78%, oxygen 17%, carbon dioxide 4%.

5. (*a*) digestive juices and the hormone insulin, which converts excess blood sugar into glycogen; (*b*) the iodine-containing hormone thyroxin, which controls the body's metabolism.

6. An average man takes fifteen or sixteen, a woman eighteen.

7. (*a*) 7–9 pints; (*b*) plasma – 92% water.

8. Thirty-two. Incisor, canine, molar, premolar.

9. (*a*) kneecap; (*b*) thigh-bone;
   (*c*) collar-bone; (*d*) shoulder-blade.

10. (*a*) leg; (*b*) wrist;
    (*c*) upper arm; (*d*) forearm.

11. In the small intestine.

12. Drinking too much water does no harm. The body needs about 1 pint for each 1000 calories of food eaten. Drinking only 90% of this will cause exhaustion and drinking 80% or less will cause serious illness.

The BRITISH WEATHER

1. Which on average are the three wettest months of the year?

2. If lightning precedes thunder by 20 seconds how far away is the storm?

3. Which on average is the coldest month and which is the warmest month of the year?

4. When the sun is overhead what percentage of its heat reaches the ground?　100　90　80　70　60　50

5. What is the average decrease in temperature for each increase in height above sea-level of 1000 feet?

6. What on average are the odds against one being struck by lightning in any year? 100:1　　500:1　　200,000:1　1 million:1　　5 million:1　　50 million:1

7. When snow melts, how many inches of it will produce 1 inch of water?　20　15　10　8　5

8. Over the year as a whole, from which direction are winds most frequent?

9. What are depressions, anticyclones and fronts?

10. If you stand with your back to the wind on which side is the area of low pressure?

11. What is: (*a*) hoar-frost; (*b*) glazed frost?

12. Put these areas in order of highest annual rainfall. Cornwall, East Anglia, Lake District, Hampshire.

The BRITISH WEATHER

1. August, October and December.

2. 4 miles. (Sound takes about 5 seconds to travel 1 mile.)

3. January is the coldest and July is the warmest.

4. 70%.

5. 3° Fahrenheit (1.7° Centigrade).

6. 5 million:1.

7. About 10 inches.

8. South-west.

9. Depressions are areas where the atmospheric pressure is low relative to surrounding areas; they are also known as lows or cyclones. Anticyclones are areas where the pressure is high relative to surrounding areas. Fronts are lines of separation at the earth's surface between cold and warm masses of air.

10. On your left.

11. (a) a deposit of ice crystals formed on objects near the ground when water-vapour solidifies directly without first becoming liquid; it forms instead of dew when the dew-point is below freezing; (b) ice formed on objects on to which rain is falling when the temperature is below freezing.

12. Lake District, Cornwall, Hampshire, East Anglia.

BUILDINGS and ANCIENT MONUMENTS

1. Where and what is the Antonine Wall?

2. Which of these cities have a cathedral *and* a castle? Canterbury, Carlisle, Lincoln, Newcastle, Nottingham, Norwich, Wells, Worcester.

3. Which is the nearest town to these famous houses? (*a*) Chatsworth; (*b*) Knole; (*c*) Osborne House; (*d*) Tatton Park.

4. Which of these houses are Victorian in date? Burghley House, Hardwick Hall, Mentmore, Osborne House, Haddon Hall, Sutton Place, Waddesdon Manor.

5. How old is: (*a*) Stonehenge; (*b*) Hadrian's Wall?

6. What is a bailey?

7. Of which Age (Stone, Bronze or Iron) are: (*a*) round barrows; (*b*) long barrows; (*c*) hill-forts?

8. Which is the nearest town to these castles? (*a*) Pevensey; (*b*) Powis; (*c*) Rockingham; (*d*) Leeds.

9. What, on the outside of a church, is a: (*a*) gargoyle; (*b*) buttress; (*c*) finial?

10. What is a: (*a*) transept; (*b*) clerestory?

11. Which castle: (*a*) has a leaning tower; (*b*) is the largest inhabited castle in the world?

12. What ancient monument would you expect to see at: (*a*) Maiden Castle, Dorset; (*b*) Fishbourne, near Chichester, West Sussex?

BUILDINGS and
ANCIENT MONUMENTS

1. A Roman wall built c. AD 140; it ran from the Forth to the Clyde and parts of it survive. It was a turf rampart with a stone base and a ditch.

2. Canterbury, Carlisle, Lincoln, Newcastle and Norwich.

3. (a) Bakewell; (b) Sevenoaks;
   (c) Cowes; (d) Knutsford.

4. Mentmore, Osborne House and Waddesdon Manor.

5. (a) c. 3100 BC – c. 1800 BC; (b) c. AD 122 – c. AD 128.

6. The court or enclosure within the walls of a castle outside the keep.

7. (a) Bronze; (b) Stone; (c) Iron.

8. (a) Eastbourne; (b) Welshpool;
   (c) Corby; (d) Maidstone.

9. (a) rain-water spout carved into a grotesque human or animal shape;
   (b) brickwork or masonry built against a wall to give it strength;
   (c) ornament crowning a gable, canopy or tower.

10. (a) the transverse arm of a cruciform church;
    (b) the upper storey of a nave, pierced with windows.

11. (a) Caerphilly; (b) Windsor.

12. (a) a large Iron Age hill-fort;
    (b) a Roman palace built c. AD 75.

5. Questions

The CINEMA

1. What are the four film categories used by the British Board of Film Censors?

2. What do these titles refer to? (*a*) *The African Queen;* (*b*) *The General;* (*c*) *Genevieve;* (*d*) *The Spirit of St Louis.*

3. Which of these films are westerns? *Midnight Cowboy, Shane, True Grit, Oklahoma!, The Big Country, Niagara.*

4. Which of these films are musicals? *The Philadelphia Story, High Society, Oliver!, West Side Story, Grease.*

5. Which of these are war films? *North by North-west, Von Ryan's Express, Blow Up, The Longest Day, Hondo.*

6. Which of these are James Bond films? *Never Say Die, Never Say Never Again, You Only Live Twice, Gold.*

7. These films are about the same length. How long? *Lawrence of Arabia, Gone with the Wind, Ben Hur* (1959).

8. Which of these are silent films? *Intolerance, Greed, Limelight, Queen Christina, Modern Times, Strike.*

9. Which of these films are comedies? *Some Like It Hot, The Navigator, The Paleface, Rififi, Oh Mr Porter.*

10. In which countries are these films set? (*a*) *The Bridge on the River Kwai;* (*b*) *A Bridge Too Far;* (*c*) *Topkapi.*

11. What was: (*a*) *King Kong;* (*b*) *Moby Dick;* (*c*) *Dumbo;* (*d*) *Harvey*?

12. Who was: (*a*) *The Third Man;* (*b*) *A Man For All Seasons;* (*c*) *The Plainsman;* (*d*) *Our Man in Havana*?

The CINEMA

1. U = Universal;
   PG = Parental Guidance;
   15 = Fifteen and over;
   18 = Eighteen and over.

2. (*a*) steamboat; (*b*) railway engine; (*c*) veteran car; (*d*) Lindbergh's aeroplane.

3. *Shane, True Grit* and *The Big Country.*

4. *High Society, Oliver!, West Side Story* and *Grease.*

5. *Von Ryan's Express* and *The Longest Day.*

6. *Never Say Never Again* and *You Only Live Twice.*

7. About 3 hours and 40 minutes.

8. *Intolerance, Greed, Modern Times* and *Strike.*

9. *Some Like It Hot, The Navigator, The Paleface* and *Oh Mr Porter.*

10. (*a*) Burma; (*b*) Holland; (*c*) Turkey.

11. (*a*) giant ape;
    (*b*) whale;
    (*c*) baby elephant;
    (*d*) rabbit.

12. (*a*) Orson Welles as Graham Greene's Harry Lime;
    (*b*) Paul Scofield as Robert Bolt's Sir Thomas More;
    (*c*) Gary Cooper as 'Wild Bill' Hickok;
    (*d*) Alec Guinness as Graham Greene's James Wormold.

COLLECTING LARGE THINGS

1. What is a: (*a*) canterbury; (*b*) chaise longue?

2. What are these pieces of furniture?
   (*a*) armoire; (*b*) commode; (*c*) fauteuil.

3. What is the difference between a tallboy, a lowboy and a whatnot?

4. When did these styles flourish?
   (*a*) art deco; (*b*) *art nouveau*.

5. What measurement mainly determines the quality of an antique carpet?

6. With which subjects are these artists associated?
   (*a*) Sir Alfred Munnings;
   (*b*) Sir Anthony van Dyck.

7. Put these map-makers in correct chronological order. John Cary, Christopher Saxton, John Ogilby.

8. In which craft was Thomas Tompion pre-eminent and when did he flourish?

9. What is a davenport?

10. What are these pieces of furniture?
    (*a*) chiffonier; (*b*) torchère; (*c*) escritoire.

11. Put these Chinese periods in correct chronological order. Ming, T'ang, Sung, Ch'ing.

12. For what was Thomas Chippendale famous and when did he flourish?

COLLECTING LARGE THINGS

1. (*a*) stand with partitions to hold music or magazines;
   (*b*) sofa or long chair, with a rest at one end.

2. (*a*) large wardrobe;
   (*b*) chest of drawers;
   (*c*) armchair.

3. A tallboy is a tall chest of drawers, a lowboy is a low chest
   of drawers or table with drawers, and a whatnot is an
   open stand with shelves.

4. (*a*) 1920s and 1930s; (*b*) c. 1880 to c. 1915.

5. The number of knots to the square inch, about 250 being
   the finest quality.

6. (*a*) horses; (*b*) portraits.

7. Christopher Saxton c. 1542–1610, John Ogilby 1600–76,
   John Cary c. 1754–1835.

8. Clock-making; late seventeenth and early eighteenth
   century.

9. Small ornamental writing-table with drawers.

10. (*a*) small cupboard with a top forming a sideboard;
    (*b*) tall lamp-stand;
    (*c*) writing-desk or bureau.

11. T'ang 618–906, Sung 960–1279, Ming 1368–1644, Ch'ing
    1644–1911.

12. Furniture-making; eighteenth century.

COLLECTING SMALL THINGS

1. In which of these years were the following objects introduced to Great Britain? 1840 1843 1870
   (*a*) postcard; (*b*) Christmas card; (*c*) adhesive postage stamp.

2. What is majolica?

3. What are netsuke?

4. What is the best way to tell hard (true) porcelain from soft (artificial) porcelain?

5. What is Goss china?

6. What is cloisonné?

7. In an antiquarian bookseller's catalogue what do these abbreviations mean?
   (*a*) a.e.g.;   (*b*) d.w. (or d.j.);   (*c*) o.p.;   (*d*) e.p.

8. What has happened to old books that are:
   (*a*) foxed;   (*b*) wormed;   (*c*) cropped?

9. Which of these British stamps is the most valuable (unused)?   1840 1d black;   1840 2d blue;
   1856 1s green;   1882 £1 brown;   1882 £5 orange.

10. What are Stevengraphs?

11. Which one of these British pennies is extremely scarce?
    1927 1930 1933 1938 1940

12. What is the name for small wooden domestic utensils such as spoons, bowls and cups?

7. Answers

COLLECTING SMALL THINGS

1. (*a*) 1870; (*b*) 1843; (*c*) 1840.

2. A type of Italian glazed earthenware.

3. Small Japanese carvings of wood, ivory or bone.

4. Soft porcelain can be cut with a file.

5. Miniature porcelain objects with crests or coats of arms of towns and cities, originally sold as tourist souvenirs.

6. A type of decorative enamel-ware.

7. (*a*) all edges gilt;
   (*b*) dust-wrapper (or dust-jacket);
   (*c*) out of print;
   (*d*) end-paper.

8. (*a*) the paper is discoloured or stained with brownish-yellow spots;
   (*b*) the paper has holes where bookworms have eaten through it;
   (*c*) the page margins have been cut down, even sometimes into the text.

9. 1882 £1 brown.

10. Woven-silk pictures made by Thomas Stevens of Coventry.

11. 1933.

12. Treen.

COOKERY

1. Which one of these dishes *must* be cooked with wine? lobster thermidor, tortilla espagnol, *coq au vin*.

2. What is the name given to a dish cooked with a crisp brown crust of bread crumbs or cheese?

3. What is the name for small cubes of fried or toasted bread eaten usually with soups?

4. What are: (*a*) entrées; (*b*) hors-d'oeuvres?

5. What is a: (*a*) vol-au-vent; (*b*) soufflé?

6. What is a: (*a*) *purée*; (*b*) mousse?

7. Name a mineral that is not dissolved out when green vegetables are cooked.

8. What are: (*a*) macédoine; (*b*) tournedos?

9. Without breaking its shell how can you tell:
   (*a*) the freshness of an egg;
   (*b*) a hard-boiled egg from a raw egg?

10. What ingredients are needed for making pancakes?

11. What is the name for: (*a*) cooking meat or vegetables until tender in a covered pan, then browning in the oven with the lid removed; (*b*) the pouring of liquid, usually fat or gravy, over food during cooking?

12. Which of these are herbs and which are spices?
    (*a*) capers; (*b*) caraway; (*c*) nutmeg; (*d*) sage; (*e*) marjoram; (*f*) mustard; (*g*) fennel; (*h*) cloves; (*i*) chives; (*j*) garlic.

COOKERY

1. *Coq au vin.*

2. *Au gratin.*

3. *Croûtons.*

4. (*a*) dishes served between the fish and meat courses;
   (*b*) dishes served before main meals as appetizers.

5. (*a*) case of puff pastry filled with savoury mixture;
   (*b*) light spongy dish usually of beaten egg-white.

6. (*a*) smooth pulp of vegetables or fruit;
   (*b*) dish of cold whipped cream and eggs flavoured with fruit, chocolate or meat *purée*.

7. Iron or calcium.

8. (*a*) small sliced mixed fruits or vegetables;
   (*b*) small thick beef fillet steaks in suet.

9. (*a*) by placing it in water containing 10% salt. If fresh it will rest on or near the bottom, if several days old it will float on top;
   (*b*) it will spin much longer because there is no liquid to retard it.

10. Flour, egg(s) and milk.

11. (*a*) braising;
    (*b*) basting.

12. (*a*) spice; (*b*) spice; (*c*) spice; (*d*) herb; (*e*) herb;
    (*f*) spice; (*g*) herb; (*h*) spice; (*i*) herb; (*j*) herb.

The COUNTRYSIDE

1. How can one tell the age of a tree?

2. In Great Britain which is the most common:
   (*a*) waterside tree; (*b*) tree in planted hedgerows?

3. Is it illegal to pick mushrooms or blackberries growing wild on private land?

4. What can one deduce about the age of fields bounded by straight hedgerows and of fields of irregular shape bounded by curving hedgerows?

5. What are Death Cap, Panther Cap, Destroying Angel and Fly Agaric, and why should you not pick them?

6. Is the foreshore (the area between low-water and high-water mark) common land?

7. What is the difference between a public footpath and a bridleway? What are your rights on the former?

8. Are you entitled to remove an obstruction on a public footpath? Are you entitled to walk round it?

9. Where may one fish without licence or restriction?

10. Which two of these berries are poisonous?
    elderberry, cowberry, privet, holly, bilberry.

11. Which four of these flowers may be picked if growing wild abundantly? daisy, mistletoe, forget-me-not, daffodil, dandelion, bluebell, thrift, groundsel.

12. Name one of the only three native British conifers.

The COUNTRYSIDE

1. Fairly accurately, when cut, by the number of rings in a cross-section of its trunk; when still standing by its circumference at shoulder-height, e.g. a tree 6 feet in circumference is about 72 years old.

2. (*a*) alder;   (*b*) hawthorn.

3. No, not unless you sell them.

4. The former are mostly the result of Parliamentary enclosure in the eighteenth and nineteenth centuries and the latter are mostly of medieval or Saxon date.

5. They are all poisonous mushrooms or toadstools.

6. No. (It belongs to the Crown who allow public access.)

7. A public footpath is only for walkers; a bridleway may also be used by horse-riders and cyclists. Your rights on a public footpath are restricted to walking; you may not picnic or play games etc.

8. You may remove only as much of the obstruction as is necessary to allow you to pass. You may walk round it even if it means walking across private land, e.g. round the edge of a field to avoid crops.

9. In the sea (but not from a pier) and in tidal waters.

10. Privet and holly.

11. Daisy, forget-me-not, dandelion and groundsel.

12. Scots pine, yew and juniper.

CREEPY-CRAWLY CREATURES

1. What is the essential difference between flies and other winged insects?

2. (a) What is the definition of an insect?
   (b) Which is the largest British insect?

3. (a) Do wasps and bees die after stinging?
   (b) Which type of bee cannot sting?

4. Which is the only poisonous snake in Britain? Why are snakes more active in summer than in winter?

5. Where do flies and wasps go in the winter?

6. Which insects carry and spread these diseases?
   (a) sleeping sickness; (b) yellow fever; (c) malaria; (d) plague; (e) typhus.

7. Do moths eat clothes?

8. Which type of insect fits this description?
   'Body ovoid; pair of tubercles at posterior end of abdomen; sucking mouth-parts; found on plants'.

9. What harm is done by the common house-fly?

10. Which of these are harmful to plants?
    centipede, millepede, wireworm, earthworm, earwig, slug.

11. Which of these do *not* bite or sting?
    crane-fly, flea, head-louse, silver-fish.

12. What happens to insects when they are subjected to high or low temperatures?

CREEPY-CRAWLY CREATURES

1. True flies have only one pair of wings; the others have two pairs.

2. (*a*) an invertebrate with a body in three sections and usually three pairs of legs and one or two pairs of wings; (*b*) the Death's-head Hawk-moth.

3. (*a*) wasps do not but bees usually do; (*b*) the drone (male bees and wasps have no stings).

4. The adder. They are cold-blooded animals and therefore more active in warm weather.

5. Mature flies die in the winter. (The flies that appear in the spring come from last autumn's eggs.) Worker wasps die in winter. The queens spend the winter in sheltered spots.

6. (*a*) tsetse fly; (*b*) mosquito; (*c*) mosquito; (*d*) flea; (*e*) body-louse.

7. No. The larvae eat clothes.

8. Aphid.

9. It spreads the bacteria of diseases.

10. Millepede, wireworm, earwig and slug.

11. Crane-fly and silver-fish.

12. They are sensitive to high temperatures (dead in 30 minutes at 60° Centigrade) and low temperatures (stop moving and laying eggs below 10° Centigrade).

11. Questions

The laws of CRICKET

1. In how many ways can a batsman be given out?

2. May a fieldsman stop the ball by throwing his cap on it? If not what is the penalty for doing so?

3. How does an umpire signal the following?
   (*a*) boundary six;
   (*b*) leg-bye;
   (*c*) no-ball.

4. How many minutes is a new batsman allowed from the fall of a wicket to stepping on to the field?

5. How many overs must be bowled in the last hour of a first-class match?

6. Does the ball become 'dead' whenever the wicket is broken?

7. When does the ball cease to be 'dead'?

8. What is the limitation on fieldsmen on the 'on' side of the wicket in a first-class match?

9. After the toss may a captain make a change to his nominated team?

10. (*a*) When may an injured batsman resume his innings?
    (*b*) When may a batsman retire?

11. What is the lead in runs required to enforce the follow-on in: (*a*) Test matches; (*b*) three-day matches; (*c*) two-day matches?

12. What is the definition of a 'wide ball'?

The laws of CRICKET

1. Ten. (Bowled, timed out, caught, handled the ball, hit wicket, hit the ball twice, leg before wicket, run out, stumped and obstructed the field.)

2. No. The penalty is five runs to the batting side.

3. (*a*) raises both his arms above his head;
   (*b*) touches a raised knee with his hand;
   (*c*) extends one arm horizontally.

4. Two.

5. Twenty.

6. Only when a batsman is out by its being broken.

7. When the bowler starts his run-up or bowling action.

8. A maximum of two behind the popping-crease at the moment of delivery.

9. Yes, with the other captain's consent.

10. (*a*) at the fall of any wicket;
    (*b*) at any time.

11. (*a*) 200;
    (*b*) 150;
    (*c*) 100.

12. A ball bowled so high over or so wide of the wicket that in the opinion of the umpire it passes out of the reach of the striker standing in a normal guard position.

DATES and ANNIVERSARIES

1. What determines the date of Easter in any year?

2. How is the date of Whit Sunday (*not* the Whitsun holiday) determined?

3. Between which dates is grouse-shooting legal?

4. Which are the longest and shortest days of the year in the British Isles?

5. Does the shortest day coincide with the day that has the earliest sunset?

6. How many months have 31 days each?

7. What is the date of:
   (*a*) Guy Fawkes Night;   (*b*) Twelfth Night;
   (*c*) St Valentine's Day; (*d*) Hallowe'en?

8. When is American Independence Day?

9. What is the date of:
   (*a*) St Patrick's Day;   (*b*) St George's Day;
   (*c*) St Andrew's Day; (*d*) St David's Day?

10. What is the special significance of these dates?
    (*a*) 21 April;
    (*b*) 15 July;
    (*c*) 15 September;
    (*d*) 26 December.

11. When did Great Britain enter World Wars I and II?

12. What were the dates of VE Day and VJ Day (1945)?

DATES and ANNIVERSARIES

1. Easter Sunday is the first Sunday after the first full moon following the vernal equinox, which is the day the sun crosses the Equator (usually 21 March).

2. It is seven weeks after Easter Sunday.

3. 12 August to 10 December inclusive.

4. The longest day falls on either 21 or 22 June and the shortest day on either 21 or 22 December.

5. No. (In London the earliest sunset is on either 12 or 13 December.)

6. Seven. (January, March, May, July, August, October and December.)

7. (a) 5 November;   (b) 5 January;
   (c) 14 February;   (d) 31 October.

8. 4 July.

9. (a) 17 March;   (b) 23 April;
   (c) 30 November;   (d) 1 March.

10. (a) Queen's birthday;
    (b) St Swithin's Day;
    (c) Battle of Britain Day;
    (d) Boxing Day.

11. World War I: 4 August 1914;
    World War II: 3 September 1939.

12. VE Day was 8 May and VJ Day was 14 August.

ETIQUETTE and HONOURS

1. Give the correct order of precedence of the peerage. viscount, marquess, baron, earl, duke.

2. Give the correct name for the wife of each of those.

3. How should one address the following in an informal letter? (*a*) Sir John Smith; (*b*) Lord Smith; (*c*) Admiral John Smith; (*d*) Admiral Sir John Smith.

4. How should one address the following on an envelope? (*a*) the Archbishop of Canterbury; (*b*) a mayor of a borough; (*c*) a viscount.

5. Give the correct order of precedence of these decorations and honours: OM VC CBE KG CH GC.

6. How should one address the Queen if presented?

7. How should one end a business letter that begins: (*a*) Dear Sir; (*b*) Dear Mr Smith?

8. Who should send out the invitations to a wedding?

9. Who should pay for these at a wedding? (*a*) reception; (*b*) ring; (*c*) cake; (*d*) church service.

10. In what order should these letters be placed after a person's name? FRS QC MP MA OBE JP.

11. Give the equivalent ranks in the Army and the Royal Air Force to: (*a*) admiral; (*b*) captain; (*c*) lieutenant.

12. How should one address the following in speech? (*a*) duke; (*b*) baronet; (*c*) archbishop; (*d*) bishop.

ETIQUETTE and HONOURS

1. Duke, marquess, earl, viscount, baron.

2. Duchess, marchioness, countess, viscountess, baroness.

3. (*a*) Dear Sir John;
   (*b*) Dear Lord Smith;
   (*c*) Dear Admiral Smith;
   (*d*) Dear Sir John.

4. (*a*) The Most Reverend and Right Honourable the Lord Archbishop of Canterbury;
   (*b*) The Worshipful the Mayor of ... ;
   (*c*) The Right Honourable the Viscount ....

5. VC GC KG OM CH CBE.

6. First say 'Your Majesty' and subsequently 'Ma'am'.

7. (*a*) Yours faithfully;
   (*b*) Yours sincerely.

8. The bride's parents, in particular her mother.

9. (*a*) bride's parents; (*b*) bridegroom;
   (*c*) bride's parents; (*d*) bridegroom.

10. OBE QC JP MA FRS MP.

11. (*a*) general and air chief marshal;
    (*b*) colonel and group captain;
    (*c*) captain and flight lieutenant.

12. (*a*) Your Grace;   (*b*) Sir (with his Christian name);
    (*c*) Your Grace;   (*d*) My Lord.

FIRST AID

1. Can snake bites prove fatal in Britain?

2. Which of these is the correct treatment for a burn?
   (*a*) apply cotton wool or adhesive plaster;
   (*b*) apply ointment;
   (*c*) hold under cold running water.

3. Should a frost-bitten hand or foot be warmed slowly or quickly?

4. Should a person suffering from shock be given anything to drink?

5. How can you tell for sure whether a person is breathing or not?

6. What is the correct treatment for hypothermia?

7. What causes a scald as distinct from a burn?

8. Should a blister ever be broken?

9. What is the best treatment for someone who has fainted?

10. What is the difference between a closed fracture and an open fracture?

11. Should a tourniquet be used to stop bleeding from a wound?

12. A good first aid kit should enable you to treat most minor injuries. Name six items that should be part of a good first aid kit.

FIRST AID

1. Yes, but rarely. Adders are the only poisonous snakes.

2. (*c*).

3. Slowly.

4. No.

5. By placing your ear close to the person's mouth or nose and can feel or hear breaths, or you can see the chest moving.

6. Warm the person slowly, e.g. by wrapping in blankets, and give a warm drink (but not alcohol).

7. A burn is caused by dry heat (or cold), e.g. fire or hot metal, a scald by moist heat, e.g. steam or water.

8. Only if it is liable to damage, or if it is very painful.

9. Lie the person down with legs above head level and loosen tight clothing.

10. In a closed fracture the bone is broken but the skin is undamaged; in an open fracture the bone sticks through the skin or there is a wound.

11. No, pressure should be applied directly to the wound.

12. Adhesive dressings or plasters, sterile dressings, cotton wool, crepe bandages, triangular bandages, painkillers, scissors, tweezers, safety-pins, antihistamine cream, calamine lotion, antiseptics.

FOOD HYGIENE

1. Are all bacteria killed by: (*a*) high temperatures; (*b*) low temperatures; (*c*) detergents?

2. Why should raw meat be stored on the bottom shelf of a refrigerator?

3. What should be done after cooking raw food, if it is to be eaten cold?

4. What should be done with hot food, if it is to be eaten hot?

5. Can one always tell for certain whether a food is fit to eat?

6. (*a*) Should defrosted frozen food be refrozen?
   (*b*) Should cooked food be reheated?

7. Which is the most hygienic method of drying: (*a*) one's hands; (*b*) crockery?

8. How can one tell whether rats and mice have been in the pantry?

9. Which is the best material for sinks?

10. (*a*) What is the main precaution to be taken with frozen poultry before cooking?
    (*b*) Should poultry be defrosted in an oven?

11. (*a*) Why should fruit *not* be cooked in copper pans?
    (*b*) How does one recognise a 'blown' can of food?

12. Name two of the three most common kitchen pests.

FOOD HYGIENE

1. (*a*) yes (in 30 minutes at 65° Centigrade if moisture is present, but spores take 3 to 5 hours at 100° Centigrade); (*b*) low temperatures never kill all bacteria; (*c*) no.

2. To prevent blood dripping on and contaminating other foods.

3. It should be cooled to below 5° Centigrade to prevent the growth of bacteria.

4. It should be kept above 65° Centigrade until eaten, or be eaten within 30 minutes.

5. Not always (but one can often tell for sure when a food is unfit to eat).

6. (*a*) no; (*b*) no.

7. (*a*) hot-air drying;
   (*b*) allowing to dry naturally.

8. By their droppings and by gnawed food and packets.

9. Stainless steel.

10. (*a*) it should be thoroughly defrosted;
    (*b*) no.

11. (*a*) the acid may dissolve the copper and cause poisoning;
    (*b*) it bulges at the ends or sides (caused by microbes in the can producing gas).

12. Flies, ants and cockroaches.

FOOD for THOUGHT

1. Milk contains what percentage of water?
   60   75   80   87   96

2. Which one of these contains most protein?
   Cheddar cheese, cod fillets, soya beans, chicken.

3. What is haggis?

4. Which one of these contains most fat?
   pork sausage, olive oil, butter, margarine.

5. Distinguish between semolina, tapioca and sago.

6. Which one of these contains most carbohydrate?
   bread, Dundee cake, boiled potatoes, rice.

7. How many pints of milk does it take to make:
   (*a*) 1 pound of butter; (*b*) 4 ounces of cream?

8. Which one of these will give most energy, weight for
   weight? cheese sandwich, cream of tomato soup, chocolate
   ice cream, chocolate cream biscuits.

9. Which one of these contains most cholesterol?
   butter, cheese, eggs, liver, fish roe, kidneys.

10. Which of these foods is a good source of:
    (*a*) vitamin A; (*b*) vitamin B1; (*c*) vitamin C; (*d*) calcium?
    black currants, milk, wholemeal bread, cod-liver oil.

11. What are: (*a*) Bath chaps; (*b*) Bath Olivers; (*c*) Bath buns?

12. What is the name for fresh milk artificially curdled by
    harmless bacteria to produce a nourishing food?

FOOD for THOUGHT

1. 87%.

2. Soya beans (40%).

3. A mixture of oatmeal, suet, liver, heart and lights, boiled in the skin of a sheep's stomach like a large sausage.

4. Olive oil (100%).

5. Semolina consists of hard portions of wheat collected in the form of rounded grains, tapioca is a starch obtained from the roots of the cassava plant and sago is a starch produced from the pith of certain palm trees.

6. Rice (87%).

7. (*a*) about 18; (*b*) about 3.

8. Chocolate cream biscuits.

9. Eggs.

10. (*a*) cod-liver oil;
    (*b*) wholemeal bread;
    (*c*) black currants;
    (*d*) milk.

11. (*a*) pieces of pig's cheek salted and smoked;
    (*b*) biscuits made from flour, butter, yeast and milk;
    (*c*) yellow buns with sugar on top.

12. Yoghurt.

FOREIGN WORDS and PHRASES

1. What is the difference between à la carte and table d'hôte meals?

2. Describe these persons: (*a*) *enfant terrible;* (*b*) *bête noire;* (*c*) *éminence grise;* (*d*) bon vivant.

3. Where is something that is: (*a*) *in situ;* (*b*) *chez nous?*

4. Translate these items on a French menu: (*a*) *consommé;* (*b*) *escargots;* (*c*) *rognons;* (*d*) *fraises;* (*e*) *crevettes grises;* (*f*) *jambon;* (*g*) *fromage;* (*h*) *framboises.*

5. What do these musical terms mean? (*a*) *lento;* (*b*) *legato;* (*c*) *pizzicato;* (*d*) *pianissimo.*

6. How would someone speak: (*a*) *ad lib;* (*b*) *ad infinitum?*

7. What is the meaning of: (*a*) *pièce de résistance;* (*b*) *tour de force?*

8. What is the expression for a social error or breach of etiquette, a tactless mistake or blunder?

9. What is an: (*a*) *aficionado;* (*b*) *habitué?*

10. What is the expression for: (*a*) under judicial consideration but not yet decided; (*b*) beyond someone's legal power or authority?

11. How do you say 'yes' and 'no' in: (*a*) French; (*b*) Italian; (*c*) German; (*d*) Spanish?

12. How do you say 'please' and 'thank you' in: (*a*) French; (*b*) Italian; (*c*) German; (*d*) Spanish?

FOREIGN WORDS and PHRASES

1. A la carte is a choice of separate items from a menu and table d'hôte is a set meal at a set price.

2. (*a*) one who embarrasses by tactless behaviour;
   (*b*) one who is heartily disliked;
   (*c*) one who has power or influence without office;
   (*d*) one who loves good living.

3. (*a*) in its original place; (*b*) at our house or home.

4. (*a*) clear soup; (*b*) snails; (*c*) kidneys; (*d*) strawberries;
   (*e*) shrimps; (*f*) ham; (*g*) cheese; (*h*) raspberries.

5. (*a*) slowly; (*b*) smoothly; (*c*) plucking with the fingers;
   (*d*) very softly.

6. (*a*) without preparation, improvised;
   (*b*) without limit, going on for ever.

7. (*a*) the highlight or best item; (*b*) a feat of strength or skill.

8. *Faux pas.*

9. (*a*) an enthusiast for a particular sport;
   (*b*) a resident or frequent visitor.

10. (*a*) *sub judice*; (*b*) *ultra vires.*

11. (*a*) *oui: non*; (*b*) *si: no*;
    (*c*) *ja: nein*; (*d*) *si: no.*

12. (*a*) *s'il vous plaît: merci*; (*b*) *per favore: grazie*;
    (*c*) *bitte: danke (schön)*; (*d*) *por favor: gracias.*

The rules of indoor GAMES

1. How many pieces are used in a game of:
   (*a*) chess; (*b*) draughts; (*c*) backgammon; (*d*) dominoes?

2. In correct order which are the four best scoring combinations in poker?

3. Fill in the missing numbers reading clockwise round a dartboard: 1 18 4 ? 6 10 15 ? 17 3 19 ? 16 8 11 ? 9 12 5 ?

4. What is the value of each coloured ball in snooker?

5. In contract bridge what is the ranking order of the suits after 'no trumps' when making bids?

6. In chess which piece moves: (*a*) only diagonally; (*b*) one or more squares in any direction?

7. How much 'money' does one start with in the UK version of Monopoly?

8. In solo whist how many tricks must be won in a call of: (*a*) solo; (*b*) *misère;* (*c*) *abondance?*

9. In snooker what is the penalty for potting the cue-ball direct from the break?

10. What is the best possible hand to hold in a game of cribbage with a five as the turned-up card?

11. In chess which piece always commands the same number of squares wherever it is on the board?

12. In pontoon or *vingt-et-un* what hand enables a player to become banker?

The rules of indoor GAMES

1. (*a*) 32; (*b*) 24; (*c*) 30; (*d*) 28.

2. Royal straight flush (A K Q J 10 of one suit);
   straight flush (five consecutive of one suit);
   fours (four of the same denomination);
   full house (three of one denomination and two of another).

3. 13 2 7 14 20.

4. Red – one; yellow – two; green – three; brown – four; blue – five; pink – six; black – seven.

5. From low to high: clubs, diamonds, hearts, spades.

6. (*a*) bishop;
   (*b*) queen.

7. £1500.

8. (*a*) five;
   (*b*) none;
   (*c*) nine.

9. Four points.

10. The jack of the same suit as the turned-up card and the other three fives – a total score of twenty-nine points (sixteen points for fifteens, twelve points for pairs and 'one for his nob').

11. Rook.

12. An ace with a court card or a ten.

In the GARDEN

1. What is the name for plants that live for: (*a*) only one year; (*b*) only two years; (*c*) three or more years?

2. What usually results from failure in June to thin out a heavy crop of apples?

3. What is mulch? To which plants should it be applied?

4. What are the common names for these flowers?
(*a*) antirrhinum; (*b*) calendula; (*c*) myosotis;
(*d*) helianthus.

5. Name two of the five classes of rose.

6. Which of these fertilizers contains most:
(*a*) nitrogen; (*b*) phosphates?
sulphate of ammonia, bone-meal, soot, fish-meal.

7. Which of these are evergreens?
hazel, ash, eucalyptus, alder, willow, holly.

8. Give two advantages of adding lime to the soil.

9. Which of these are annuals and which are perennials?
aster, godetia, lupin, nasturtium, primrose.

10. Which of these grow best on an acid soil and which on an alkaline soil? wallflowers, heathers, apple trees, cabbages, lawn grass.

11. What are the common names for these flowers?
(*a*) delphinium; (*b*) galanthus; (*c*) dianthus; (*d*) digitalis.

12. Which of these are sown in early spring and which in early summer? leek, swede, marrow, parsnip.

In the GARDEN

1. (*a*) annuals; (*b*) biennials; (*c*) perennials.

2. The fruit will be small and next year's crop will be poor.

3. A layer of bulky organic material placed on the soil surface. It should be applied around trees, shrubs and herbaceous perennials (*not* annuals).

4. (*a*) snapdragon; (*b*) marigold;
   (*c*) forget-me-not; (*d*) sunflower.

5. Hybrid tea, floribunda, miniature, climbers and ramblers, shrub.

6. (*a*) sulphate of ammonia; (*b*) bone-meal.

7. Eucalyptus and holly.

8. It reduces acidity, adds calcium, breaks up heavy clay, discourages pests and makes other plant foods available.

9. Annuals: godetia and nasturtium;
   perennials: aster, lupin and primrose.

10. Heathers, apple trees and lawn grass grow best on an acid soil, wallflowers and cabbages on an alkaline.

11. (*a*) larkspur; (*b*) snowdrop;
    (*c*) sweet-william; (*d*) foxglove.

12. Early spring: leek and parsnip;
    early summer: swede and marrow.

How good is your GRAMMAR?

What is wrong with each of these sentences?

1. We only saw him for the first time yesterday.

2. Having been stolen, the bank refused to cash the cheque.

3. I think I must have lost my wallet between the river or the shops.

4. Because I was so busy I had neither the time or the inclination to meet him.

5. He was given the task of taking Mrs Smith home after breaking her leg.

6. That is the man whom we think sent the letter.

7. It is one of the best books on cricket which has ever been published.

8. There will be an interval between each act.

9. Where to go and what to see was my main worry, but due to the rain we stayed at home.

10. In choosing between a silk shirt and a cotton shirt I think the former would be the best value.

11. Every member of the cricket team have been invited to the dinner.

12. The Government has decided at last. They will not give another penny.

How good is your GRAMMAR?

1. We saw him for the first time *only* yesterday.

2. Having been stolen, the cheque was refused by the bank.

3. I think I must have lost my wallet between the river *and* the shops.

4. Because I was so busy I had neither the time *nor* the inclination to meet him.

5. He was given the task of taking Mrs Smith home after her leg had been broken.

6. That is the man *who* we think sent the letter.

7. It is one of the best books on cricket *that have* ever been published.

8. There will be an interval between each act and the next act.

9. Where to go and what to see *were* my main *worries*, but *owing* to the rain we stayed at home.

10. In choosing between a silk shirt and a cotton shirt I think the former would be the *better* value.

11. Every member of the cricket team *has* been invited to the dinner.

12. The Government has decided at last. *It* will not give another penny.

Your HEALTH

1. What is: (*a*) tennis elbow; (*b*) housemaid's knee?

2. How are these diseases usually contracted?
   (*a*) malaria; (*b*) tetanus; (*c*) typhoid.

3. What is the usual method of protection from the above three diseases?

4. Which organ is affected by: (*a*) nephritis; (*b*) hepatitis?

5. What is the name for the liver disorder that: (*a*) is caused by too much alcohol; (*b*) produces a yellowish discoloration of the skin?

6. Which one of these does *not* confer lifetime immunity after having been caught once?
   chicken-pox; mumps; scarlet fever; shingles; measles.

7. Which animal is mainly responsible for giving these diseases to humans? (*a*) psittacosis; (*b*) rabies.

8. Which parts of the body are affected by:
   (*a*) gingivitis; (*b*) gout; (*c*) angina pectoris; (*d*) pleurisy?

9. What are: (*a*) hydrophobia; (*b*) halitosis; (*c*) hypochondria?

10. Can too much reading weaken your eyesight?

11. What is the name for: (*a*) a clouding of the lens of the eye that obscures vision; (*b*) inflammation of the membrane covering the front of the eye?

12. Which parts of the body are affected by:
    (*a*) laryngitis; (*b*) goitre; (*c*) colitis; (*d*) emphysema?

Your HEALTH

1. (*a*) pain in those muscles of the arm that extend the forearm, caused by strain; (*b*) inflammation or swelling near the kneecap, caused by pressure when kneeling.

2. (*a*) a bite from the anopheles mosquito;
   (*b*) bacteria entering the body via a wound;
   (*c*) contaminated food or water.

3. (*a*) anti-malaria tablets;
   (*b*) inoculation;
   (*c*) inoculation.

4. (*a*) kidney;   (*b*) liver.

5. (*a*) cirrhosis;   (*b*) jaundice.

6. Scarlet fever.

7. (*a*) parrot;   (*b*) dog.

8. (*a*) gums;   (*b*) joints;   (*c*) heart;   (*d*) lungs.

9. (*a*) another name for rabies, a disease usually fatal;
   (*b*) bad breath; (*c*) the belief that one is suffering from an illness or disease when none exists.

10. No. (Healthy eyes do not tire, but the eye muscles do especially in poor light.)

11. (*a*) cataract;
    (*b*) conjunctivitis.

12. (*a*) throat; (*b*) thyroid gland;
    (*c*) large intestine (colon); (*d*) lungs.

HOLIDAYS ABROAD

1. In which countries are these holiday resorts?
   (*a*) St-Moritz; (*b*) Benidorm; (*c*) Cannes; (*d*) Rimini.

2. How many miles by air from London (to within 100 miles) are: (*a*) Majorca; (*b*) Athens; (*c*) Paris?

3. What is the official language in: (*a*) Corfu; (*b*) Jordan; (*c*) Brazil; (*d*) Mexico; (*e*) India; (*f*) Canary Islands?

4. What is the unit of currency in: (*a*) South Africa; (*b*) Canada; (*c*) India; (*d*) Switzerland; (*e*) Finland?

5. Name five European states that have no coast (excluding former Soviet republics).

6. Which country lies between: (*a*) France and Spain; (*b*) Turkey and Rumania; (*c*) Libya and Algeria?

7. For which country do United Kingdom citizens *not* need a passport at any time?

8. Name the capital city of these countries.
   (*a*) Thailand;   (*b*) Turkey;   (*c*) Bulgaria.

9. Which one of these countries is *not* a member of the EC? Greece, Italy, Norway, Portugal, Spain.

10. How many hours in advance of or behind GMT is standard time at: (*a*) Paris; (*b*) Moscow; (*c*) New York?

11. In which countries are these holiday resorts?
    (*a*) Seefeld; (*b*) Ostend; (*c*) Estoril; (*d*) Miami.

12. How many miles by air from London (to within 250 miles) are: (*a*) Moscow; (*b*) New York; (*c*) Hong Kong?

HOLIDAYS ABROAD

1. (*a*) Switzerland; (*b*) Spain;
   (*c*) France; (*d*) Italy.

2. (*a*) 836;   (*b*) 1500;   (*c*) 215.

3. (*a*) Greek;   (*b*) Arabic;
   (*c*) Portuguese;   (*d*) Spanish;
   (*e*) Hindi;   (*f*) Spanish.

4. (*a*) rand;   (*b*) dollar;
   (*c*) rupee;   (*d*) franc;
   (*e*) markka.

5. Andorra, Austria, Czechoslovakia, Hungary, Liechten-
   stein, Luxembourg, San Marino, Switzerland, Vatican
   City.

6. (*a*) Andorra;   (*b*) Bulgaria;   (*c*) Tunisia.

7. Republic of Ireland.

8. (*a*) Bangkok;
   (*b*) Ankara;
   (*c*) Sofia.

9. Norway.

10. (*a*) plus 1 hour;
    (*b*) plus 3 hours;
    (*c*) minus 5 hours.

11. (*a*) Austria;   (*b*) Belgium;
    (*c*) Portugal;   (*d*) United States (or USA).

12. (*a*) 1557;   (*b*) 3440;   (*c*) 5990.

HOLIDAYS in the BRITISH ISLES

1. Name the counties on the south coast of England in their correct order from west to east.

2. Which holiday resort on the east coast of England faces west?

3. Which of these is furthest from and which is nearest to London by road?
   Torquay, Blackpool, York, Cardiff.

4. Which of these towns are situated on the coast?
   Ilfracombe, Stourport, Preston, Southwold, Windermere.

5. Name the highest points in England, Scotland and Wales. Which of them is the easiest to reach?

6. Which is the nearest town to these holiday attractions?
   (a) Blenheim Palace; (b) St Michael's Mount; (c) Stonehenge; (d) Whipsnade Zoo.

7. Which of these seaside resorts face north, east, south and west respectively? Blackpool, Great Yarmouth, Margate, Skegness, Hastings, Southend, Ilfracombe.

8. Which of those resorts have pleasure piers?

9. Which one has three piers and which has two piers?

10. Which of these are owned by the National Trust? The Vyne, Longleat, Blickling Hall, Woburn Abbey.

11. In which county is Alton Towers?

12. How far can one see from Snaefell, Isle of Man?

HOLIDAYS in the BRITISH ISLES

1. Cornwall, Devon, Dorset, Hampshire, West Sussex, East Sussex and Kent. (The Isle of Wight is a county to the south of Hampshire.)

2. Hunstanton, Norfolk.

3. Blackpool is furthest (about 225 miles) and Cardiff is nearest (about 167 miles).

4. Ilfracombe and Southwold.

5. England – Scafell Pike; Scotland – Ben Nevis; Wales – Snowdon. Snowdon is the easiest walk and there is also a railway to the summit.

6. (*a*) Woodstock; (*b*) Marazion; (*c*) Amesbury; (*d*) Dunstable.

7. North – Margate and Ilfracombe; east – Skegness and Great Yarmouth; south – Hastings and Southend; west – Blackpool.

8. Blackpool, Great Yarmouth, Hastings and Southend.

9. Blackpool has three piers and Great Yarmouth has two piers.

10. The Vyne and Blickling Hall.

11. Staffordshire.

12. On a clear day one can see the mountains of the Lake District in England, the Mull of Galloway in Scotland, the mountains in North Wales and the Mourne Mountains in Ireland.

Your HOUSE

1. Why do houses have cavity walls?

2. After moving into a house you discover dry rot. Can you sue the previous owner?

3. If you had a survey and dry rot was not mentioned in the surveyor's report what can you do?

4. Many houses are referred to as 'listed' buildings. What is a 'listed' building?

5. Which one of these needs planning permission?
   (*a*) extension to the front of a house;
   (*b*) new staircase.

6. Are you legally obliged to have your house or its contents insured?

7. What is the main difference between dry and wet rot?

8. What may happen if the air in your house is too moist and there is condensation? How can you get rid of moist air?

9. What may happen if the air is too dry? How can you increase the humidity?

10. Up to what height is planning permission unnecessary for a new summer-house?

11. How does freehold differ from leasehold?

12. When you sell a house are you entitled to remove: (*a*) central heating; (*b*) carpets; (*c*) lino; (*d*) towel rails?

Your HOUSE

1. Air is a poor conductor of heat so the air in the cavity minimizes the cold in winter and the heat in summer, and reduces the effect of damp.

2. No, you should have found out about it by having a thorough survey.

3. You can probably sue the surveyor for negligence.

4. One that is of special historic or architectural interest.

5. (*a*).

6. No, not if you are an owner-occupier.

7. Dry rot in wood thrives in damp, warm, unventilated areas; the wood develops cracks and becomes soft. Dry rot can spread through the house. Wet rot is confined to the damp area; it does not spread.

8. Ruined decorations, growth of moulds, and a musty smell. An extractor fan will remove the excess moist air.

9. Cracks in woodwork, gaps in joinery, and furniture ruined. A good humidifier will correct the humidity.

10. 4 metres.

11. Freehold confers ownership for ever; leasehold confers ownership for only a fixed period.

12. (*a*) no; (*b*) yes; (*c*) yes; (*d*) no.

INVESTING your MONEY

1. When is the interest paid on National Savings Certificates?

2. Why are National Savings Certificates attractive to people who pay income tax?

3. What is the Unlisted Securities Market?

4. Many people invest in gilt-edged stocks or 'gilts'. What is a 'gilt'?

5. If inflation was 10% per annum how many years would your capital take to halve in value?

6. What is the difference between *preference* shares and *ordinary* shares?

7. What is the difference between a *unit* trust and an *investment* trust?

8. (*a*) What sort of person gains most from an annuity?
   (*b*) What is the best age to invest in one?

9. If £1000 is invested at compound interest of 10% what will it amount to after two years (with the interest paid yearly)?

10. What would it amount to after two years with the interest paid half-yearly?

11. Are you allowed to invest money in more than one building society?

12. What is a 'bull' market and what is a 'bear' market?

INVESTING your MONEY

1. When they are cashed in.

2. The interest on them is free of income tax.

3. The market for shares in small companies that do not qualify for a full quotation on the Stock Exchange.

4. A stock issued by the government that has a fixed rate of interest and is redeemable within a certain number of years.

5. Just over $6\frac{1}{2}$ years.

6. Preference shares pay a fixed rate of dividend which has priority over the dividend on ordinary shares. Ordinary shares pay a variable dividend depending on whether the company is successful or not.

7. A unit trust is a trust that invests in a portfolio of shares managed by the unit trust managers.
An investment trust is a public company whose assets consist wholly of shares in other companies.

8. (a) one who survives beyond normal life expectancy;
(b) the older you are, the higher the annual income.

9. £1210.00.

10. £1215.50.

11. Yes.

12. A 'bull' market occurs when prices of shares are rising and a 'bear' market when they are falling.

Against the LAW

1. May one park on a common, heath or public place providing the car is within 15 yards of a highway?

2. May a Christian name or surname be changed at will?

3. What is the difference between assault and battery?

4. Can a woman sue a man for broken engagement (breach of promise) or vice versa?

5. To avoid misrepresentation goods must fulfil three conditions when sold to customers. Name one of them.

6. If you are the owner of an article that is being auctioned, are you allowed to bid yourself, in order to push up the price?

7. How long can a suspect be detained without charge at a police station?

8. What is the difference between libel and slander?

9. If a careless waiter spills soup over you, can you sue the restaurant? If your hostess at a private party does the same, can you sue her?

10. What is the legal effect of a 'Trespassers will be prosecuted' notice?

11. May a man marry his: (*a*) niece; (*b*) brother's widow; (*c*) first cousin; (*d*) granddaughter; (*e*) aunt?

12. Does the law relating to 'merchantable quality' apply to goods bought at auctions?

Against the LAW

1. No, it is trespassing unless a notice says otherwise.

2. Christian names of unbaptised people and surnames may be changed without legal formality. Christian names of baptised people may be changed only by Act of Parliament, at confirmation or on adoption.

3. Assault is a threat to use force or cause bodily injury. Battery is the actual use of force. Common assault covers both crimes.

4. No.

5. They must be: (a) of merchantable quality; (b) fit for the purpose for which they were bought; (c) as described by the seller.

6. No, not unless it is stated in the catalogue or by the auctioneer that you will do so.

7. 24 hours, unless it is a serious offence, in which case it can be extended to a maximum of 96 hours.

8. Libel is written, recorded or broadcast, and slander is spoken defamation.

9. Yes and no respectively.

10. None. Trespass is not a criminal offence, only a civil offence, i.e. one can be sued for damages but not prosecuted. You can be ejected if you refuse to go.

11. (a) no; (b) yes; (c) yes; (d) no; (e) no.

12. No.

LONDON

1. Where are these hospitals?
   (*a*) St Bartholomew's; (*b*) St Thomas's; (*c*) Guy's.

2. Who lives at: (*a*) Buckingham Palace; (*b*) 10 Downing Street; (*c*) Mansion House; (*d*) Lambeth Palace?

3. Where and when do these take place? (*a*) Trooping the Colour; (*b*) Lord Mayor's Show; (*c*) State Opening of Parliament.

4. What do these markets specialise in?
   (*a*) New Covent Garden; (*b*) Smithfield.

5. Name the largest park in London and its lake.

6. In which streets are these theatres?
   (*a*) Adelphi; (*b*) Coliseum; (*c*) Garrick; (*d*) Globe.

7. Where are these? (*a*) Domesday Book; (*b*) Rosetta Stone.

8. Where are: (*a*) Harrods;   (*b*) Selfridges?

9. Name these ships that can be seen in London: (*a*) was built for Scott's first Antarctic expedition; (*b*) last of the tea-clippers; (*c*) largest-ever Navy cruiser.

10. Which street is associated with:
    (*a*) newspapers;   (*b*) tailoring;   (*c*) diamonds?

11. (*a*) In which park are the Zoological Gardens?
    (*b*) In which gardens is the Albert Memorial?

12. Which two famous attractions adjoin each other in Marylebone Road?

LONDON

1. (*a*) West Smithfield (between Little Britain and Giltspur Street); (*b*) Lambeth Palace Road, Lambeth; (*c*) St Thomas Street (near London Bridge station).

2. (*a*) the Queen; (*b*) the Prime Minister; (*c*) the Lord Mayor; (*d*) the Archbishop of Canterbury.

3. (*a*) Horse Guards Parade, on the Queen's official birthday, early June; (*b*) Guildhall to the Law Courts, second Saturday in November; (*c*) Buckingham Palace to the Houses of Parliament, October or November or after an election.

4. (*a*) fruit and vegetables;   (*b*) meat.

5. Hyde Park; Serpentine.

6. (*a*) Strand; (*b*) St Martin's Lane; (*c*) Charing Cross Road; (*d*) Shaftesbury Avenue.

7. (*a*) Public Record Office;
   (*b*) British Museum.

8. (*a*) Brompton Road;   (*b*) Oxford Street.

9. (*a*) RRS *Discovery*;
   (*b*) *Cutty Sark*;
   (*c*) HMS *Belfast*.

10. (*a*) Fleet Street;   (*b*) Savile Row;   (*c*) Hatton Garden.

11. (*a*) Regents Park;   (*b*) Kensington Gardens.

12. Madame Tussaud's and the London Planetarium.

Using a MAP

All the questions refer to Ordnance Survey maps.

1. What do these abbreviations mean?
   (*a*) PH;   (*b*) TH;   (*c*) MS;   (*d*) PC.

2. What is the meaning of a white 'P' within a blue square on 1:50,000-scale maps?

3. What name has been given to the current 1:50,000-scale maps?

4. What might happen if you ignored the words 'Danger Area' marked on some maps?

5. What is a bench-mark (abbreviation BM)?

6. What is the difference between a small black square with a cross and a small black circle with a cross?

7. In which colours are these shown on 1:50,000-scale maps? (*a*) motorways; (*b*) 'A'-class roads; (*c*) 'B'-class roads; (*d*) unclassified or minor roads.

8. What is the largest-scale map published?

9. What is the largest scale at which the *whole* country is covered?

10. What sort of area is outlined by a yellow band?

11. What is the difference between the abbreviation NT in red and NT in blue?

12. How are youth hostels shown on 1:50,000-scale maps?

Using a MAP

1. (a) public house;
   (b) town hall;
   (c) milestone;
   (d) public convenience.

2. Parking.

3. Landranger.

4. You might be hit by a bullet or blown up by a shell. 'Danger Area' usually indicates firing-ranges.

5. A horizontal mark, usually cut on buildings, that has a known height above sea-level.

6. A square with a cross represents a church with a tower and a circle with a cross a church with a spire.

7. (a) blue;
   (b) red;
   (c) orange;
   d) yellow or white.

8. 1:1250 (about 50 inches to 1 mile).

9. 1:10,000 (about 6 inches to 1 mile).

10. National Park or Forest Park.

11. NT in red = National Trust property always open; NT in blue = opening restricted.

12. A red triangle.

MATHEMATICS

1. If you drive to a shop at an average speed of 30 m.p.h. and return home at an average of 20 m.p.h. what is your average speed for the entire journey?

2. What is the difference between 2 square miles and 2 miles square?

3. How many different cricket teams can be chosen from a list of seventeen players?   17   187   1870   12,376

4. If the perimeter of a square is 36 inches what is the area of the square?

5. A coin falls heads nine times in succession. What is the probability that it will fall heads once more?

6. Before the coin-tossing began what was the probability that it would fall heads ten times?

7. If the circumference of a circle is 22 inches what is its diameter?

8. Mr. Jones has two children. What is the probability that they are both boys?

9. What is the lowest number into which all the numbers from one to ten can be divided?

10. Smith walks to his office, which is 4 miles away, in 80 minutes. How fast does he walk?

11. What is the square root of 625?

12. What does Pythagoras's Theorem state?

MATHEMATICS

1. 24 m.p.h. (*Not* 25 m.p.h. Suppose the distance is 10 miles. Then the outward journey would take 20 minutes and the homeward journey 30 minutes. So 20 miles in 50 minutes is an average of 24 m.p.h.)

2. 2 square miles!
   (2 miles square is 4 square miles.)

3. 12,376.

4. 81 square inches.
   (Each side is 9 inches long.)

5. Evens! It can fall either heads or tails!

6. 1 in 1024. (2^{10}.)

7. About 7 inches.
   (The circumference of a circle is 22/7 times its diameter approximately.)

8. One in four.
   (*Not* one in three. They could be boy-boy, boy-girl, girl-boy or girl-girl.)

9. 2520.

10. 3 miles per hour.

11. 25.

12. In a right-angled triangle the square on the hypotenuse is equal to the sum of the squares on the other two sides.

MONEY MATTERS

1. What is the maximum legal tender in: (*a*) 1p and 2p coins; (*b*) 5p and 10p coins; (*c*) 20p and 50p coins?

2. (*a*) Are Scottish banknotes legal tender in England? (*b*) Are English banknotes legal tender in Scotland?

3. What is the main difference between a direct debit to a current account and a standing order?

4. If a bank pays out money on a forged cheque who is responsible for the loss?

5. Must a bank pay standing orders from a customer's account even if there are insufficient funds in it?

6. If a wife saves part of the housekeeping allowance to whom does it belong?

7. Is an employer obliged to pay wages to an employee who is attending for jury service?

8. (*a*) Must a cheque be written on a proper bank cheque? (*b*) Must a cheque be written in ink?

9. For what reasons can a bank dishonour a cheque?

10. Which is usually the cheapest method of borrowing money from a bank and why?

11. What is the difference between whole-life assurance and term assurance?

12. Who bears the cost of the 'free' credit available for about one month with a credit card?

MONEY MATTERS

1. (*a*) 20 pence;   (*b*) £5;   (*c*) £10.

2. (*a*) no, not even in Scotland.
   (*b*) no.

3. A direct debit can be changed without reference to the account holder. A standing order cannot be changed without his instructions.

4. The bank.

5. If there are insufficient funds in the account on the relevant date then the bank need not pay them.

6. To the husband and wife jointly.

7. No.

8. (*a*) no, legally a cheque can be written on anything provided that the writing is legible;
   (*b*) no, it can be written in pencil but obviously that can be more easily tampered with.

9. Mainly if there are insufficient cleared funds in the account or if there is a mistake on the cheque.

10. An overdraft, because interest is charged on a daily basis, i.e. on the amount owed each day.

11. In the former the sum assured is payable at death, in the latter at the end of a set number of years.

12. The retailer because he pays an agreed percentage of the retail price to the credit card company.

Your MOTOR CAR

1. What are the advantages of a radial tyre compared with a cross-ply tyre?

2. What percentage of antifreeze protects the cooling system against a temperature of minus 8° Centigrade?

3. What are the main advantages of an overdrive gear?

4. Which parts of a car are connected by the: (a) exhaust manifold; (b) inlet manifold?

5. If a car's engine cuts out suddenly is the cause likely to be electrical or mechanical?

6. Which four things on a car should be checked every day or two?

7. What is the main advantage and main disadvantage of disc brakes compared with drum brakes?

8. If while you are driving, the ignition light comes on and stays on what is the probable cause?

9. What is the name of the mechanism that allows the driving wheels to revolve at different speeds when turning corners?

10. With which countries are these cars mostly associated?
(a) Volvo; (b) Renault; (c) Skoda; (d) Mazda.

11. What is meant when an engine is said to be 1250 c.c?

12. How can you tell whether the petrol mixture is too weak or too rich?

Your MOTOR CAR

1. A radial tyre is less likely to cause skidding, has better road-holding and usually lasts longer.

2. 25%.

3. Lower fuel consumption and less engine wear.

4. (a) cylinder-head and exhaust-pipe;
   (b) cylinder-head and carburettor.

5. Electrical.

6. Tyre pressures, oil level, water level and battery electrolyte level.

7. Disc brakes do not fade as much as drum brakes because their heat is dissipated more readily, but they are not so effective at low speeds.

8. A broken fan belt, or in cars that have no fan belt the alternator drive belt.

9. Differential gear.

10. (a) Sweden;   (b) France;
    (c) Czechoslovakia;   (d) Japan.

11. The total volume of the cylinders in the engine is 1250 cubic centimetres.

12. If too weak, the engine overheats and lacks power and the sparking-plugs have a whitish appearance. If too rich, the engine runs unevenly when hot, more petrol is used and the plugs have a deposit of black soot.

MUSEUMS

1. The birthplaces of these famous men are now museums. Where are they? (*a*) Carlyle; (*b*) Dickens; (*c*) Samuel Johnson; (*d*) Gainsborough.

2. Fit these museums to their correct locations.
submarines, smuggling, mustard, bagpipes, tramways.
Norwich, Crich, Ventnor, Newcastle, Gosport.

3. What would one expect to see in the:
(*a*) Robert Opie Collection; (*b*) Shuttleworth Collection; (*c*) Donington Collection?

4. Which two comedians have a museum dedicated to them?

5. Where are the museums relating to: (*a*) Gilbert White; (*b*) Earl Mountbatten; (*c*) Jane Austen; (*d*) Grace Darling?

6. Whose museum is at Bateman's, Burwash, East Sussex?

7. In which museum is: (*a*) Stephenson's *Rocket;* (*b*) Sir Malcolm Campbell's *Bluebird?*

8. Whose birthplaces, now museums, are at: (*a*) Cockermouth; (*b*) Eastwood; (*c*) Blantyre; (*d*) Bishop's Stortford?

9. Give the location of one of the five canal museums.

10. Where are these? (*a*) National Railway Museum; (*b*) National Postal Museum; (*c*) National Lifeboat Museum.

11. Name two museums at South Kensington, London.

12. For what are these museums famous? (*a*) York Castle; (*b*)Ashmolean, Oxford; (*c*) Ironbridge Gorge.

MUSEUMS

1. (*a*) Ecclefechan, Dumfries;   (*b*) Portsmouth;
   (*c*) Lichfield; (*d*) Sudbury, Suffolk.

2. Submarines – Gosport; smuggling – Ventnor; mustard –
   Norwich; bagpipes – Newcastle; tramways – Crich.

3. (*a*) nineteenth and twentieth-century packaging;
   (*b*) historic aircraft and veteran cars;
   (*c*) Grand Prix single-seater racing-cars.

4. Laurel and Hardy (at Ulverston).

5. (*a*) Selborne, Hampshire; (*b*) Romsey, Hampshire;
   (*c*) Chawton, Hampshire; (*d*) Bamburgh, Northumberland.

6. Rudyard Kipling.

7. (*a*) Science Museum, London;
   (*b*) National Motor Museum, Beaulieu.

8. (*a*) William Wordsworth; (*b*) D.H. Lawrence; (*c*) David
   Livingstone; (*d*) Cecil Rhodes.

9. Stoke Bruerne, Ellesmere Port, Shardlow, Llangollen,
   Gloucester.

10. (*a*) York;   (*b*) London;   (*c*) Bristol.

11. Geological Museum, Natural History Museum, Victoria
    and Albert Museum, Science Museum, Wellcome
    Museum.

12. (*a*) reconstruction of a York street, old shop-fronts;
    (*b*) paintings and classical antiquities;
    (*c*) history of iron-making at Coalbrookdale.

Your NEIGHBOURS

1. Must adjoining properties be separated by a fence or wall? How can you tell who owns a boundary fence?

2. If your neighbour has regular monthly bonfires is he breaking the law?

3. If fruit from your neighbour's trees falls in your garden may you keep it?

4. If your neighbour builds an extension that overlooks your house and reduces your privacy what can you do?

5. What percentage of households have: (*a*) dogs; (*b*) cats?

6. What is the maximum height of boundary wall, fence or hedge that you may erect without permission?

7. If your neighbour's football or golf ball lands in your garden are you entitled to keep it?

8. What percentage of households in Great Britain live in detached houses?   25   19   15   10   8

9. If your neighbour's dog attacks you in your garden, is your neighbour responsible?

10. If a neighbour's tree overhangs your garden may you lop the branches yourself without notice?

11. If your neighbour's dog or cat keeps coming into your garden can you make the owner keep it away?

12. If it is your neighbour's cows that keep coming into your garden what then?

Your NEIGHBOURS

1. No law states that a boundary must be fenced.
   To determine the owner look in your title-deeds; failing that the fence probably belongs to whichever side has the fence supports.

2. No. (But if he had one every day or so there might be a good case against him.)

3. No, it belongs to your neighbour.

4. Nothing. There is no right to privacy in English law.

5. (*a*)23%; (*b*) 18%.

6. Fences and walls – 2 metres between properties and 1 metre on road frontages.
   Hedges – no restriction on height.

7. You are not entitled even to touch it but the owner may not collect it without your permission.

8. 19%.

9. Yes. If an owner allows a dog to enter any place where it is not permitted to be and there injures any person, he is guilty of an offence. (Dangerous Dogs Act 1991.)

10. Yes, but only from your garden. (The branches belong to your neighbour.)

11. No, it is up to you to fence your garden.

12. It is his responsibility to keep them away and to pay for any damage.

Too OLD or too YOUNG?

1. What are the age limits for free National Health prescriptions?

2. What is the minimum age at which one may buy these?
(*a*) cigarettes; (*b*) alcohol; (*c*) fireworks; (*d*) pet animals; (*e*) Premium Savings Bonds; (*f*) property.

3. At what age may one drive these?
(*a*) motor cycle; (*b*) motor car; (*c*) heavy goods vehicle.

4. At what age may one use a moped of up to 50 c.c?

5. What is the minimum age for: (*a*) voting; (*b*) flying an aircraft?

6. What is the minimum age at which one can become a:
(*a*) policeman; (*b*) Member of Parliament; (*c*) bookmaker?

7. At what age may: (*a*) children be employed part-time; (*b*) young persons be employed full-time?

8. What is the minimum age for obtaining:
(*a*) state pensions; (*b*) senior-citizen railcards?

9. What is the minimum age for: (*a*) making a will; (*b*) buying firearms?

10. At what age may a person get married?

11. At what age may one: (*a*) choose a doctor; (*b*) join a trade union; (*c*) have an individual passport?

12. At what age may one: (*a*) buy horror comics; (*b*) do the football pools?

Too OLD or too YOUNG?

1. 65 and over for men, 60 and over for women and under 16 for children.

2. (*a*) 16 (*b*) 18
   (*c*) 16 (*d*) 12
   (*e*) 16 (*f*) 18.

3. (*a*) 17 (*b*) 17 (*c*) 21.

4. 16.

5. (*a*) 18
   (*b*) 17.

6. (*a*) 18
   (*b*) 21
   (*c*) 21.

7. (*a*) minimum 13
   (*b*) minimum 16.

8. (*a*) 65 and over for men, 60 and over for women;
   (*b*) 60 for both men and women.

9. (*a*) 18
   (*b*) 17.

10. 16 (18 without parents' consent).

11. (*a*) 16
    (*b*) 16
    (*c*) 5 (18 without parents' consent).

12. (*a*) 16 (*b*) 18.

35. Questions

Who are these PEOPLE?

1. These people can be seen on racecourses. What are they?
   (*a*) touts;   (*b*) tick-tack men;   (*c*) tipsters.

2. Which football teams have these nicknames?
   (*a*) 'Gunners'; (*b*) 'Spurs'; (*c*) 'Hammers'; (*d*) 'Canaries'.

3. What is an: (*a*) actuary; (*b*) assayer?

4. Where do these people live?
   (*a*) Dyaks;   (*b*) Ibos;   (*c*) Sinhalese;   (*d*) Magyars.

5. What is the name for a native of: (*a*) Glasgow;
   (*b*) Manchester; (*c*) Liverpool; (*d*) Oxford?

6. What materials are handled by these people?
   (*a*) glazier;   (*b*) lapidary;   (*c*) fuller;   (*d*) brazier.

7. What do these people make?
   (*a*) cooper;   (*b*) bowyer;   (*c*) fletcher;   (*d*) joiner.

8. What is the occupation of a: (*a*) muezzin; (*b*) mahout;
   (*c*) dragoman; (*d*) shaman?

9. What are these people? (*a*) farrier; (*b*) cutler; (*c*) purser;
   (*d*) tinker.

10. What do these people collect? (*a*) philatelist;
    (*b*) numismatist; (*c*) cartophilist; (*d*) deltiologist.

11. What are: (*a*) 'yuppies'; (*b*) 'dinkies'?

12. Which parts of the body do these people study?
    (*a*) rhinologist;   (*b*) dermatologist;
    (*c*) neurologist;   (*d*) trichologist.

Who are these PEOPLE?

1. (*a*) spies who watch racehorses in training; (*b*) book-makers who signal to each other; (*c*) suppliers of tips and information about the horses in a race.

2. (*a*) Arsenal; (*b*) Tottenham Hotspur; (*c*) West Ham United; (*d*) Norwich City.

3. (*a*) one who calculates insurance risks and premiums; (*b*) a tester of metals for quality.

4. (*a*) Borneo; (*b*) Nigeria; (*c*) Sri Lanka; (*d*) Hungary.

5. (*a*) Glaswegian; (*b*) Mancunian;
   (*c*) Liverpudlian; (*d*) Oxonian.

6. (*a*) glass; (*b*) precious stones; (*c*) cloth; (*d*) brass.

7. (*a*) barrels and casks; (*b*) bows; (*c*) arrows; (*d*) furniture and woodwork.

8. (*a*) caller of Moslems to prayer; (*b*) elephant-driver; (*c*) Middle-Eastern guide; (*d*) priest or witch-doctor.

9. (*a*) one who shoes and attends to horses;
   (*b*) knife-maker or dealer;
   (*c*) ship's officer who keeps the accounts;
   (*d*) mender of pots and pans.

10. (*a*) stamps; (*b*) coins; (*c*) cigarette cards; (*d*) postcards.

11. (*a*) 'young upwardly-mobile' people;
    (*b*) people with 'dual income and no kids'.

12. (*a*) nose; (*b*) skin; (*c*) nerves; (*d*) hair.

PET ANIMALS

1. What is the average normal life expectancy of:
   (a) dogs; (b) cats; (c) rabbits?

2. Which of these cats are short-hairs?
   tabby, Persian, tortoise-shell, Siamese, chinchilla.

3. To which bird families do the canary and budgerigar belong respectively?

4. What is a: (a) borzoi; (b) gerbil?

5. When must a dog wear a collar with the name and address of its owner?

6. For how long must an animal be placed in quarantine when entering the United Kingdom?

7. What is the average normal gestation period (to within ten days) of: (a) dogs; (b) cats; (c) horses?

8. Which of these dogs are large and which are small?
   pug, mastiff, pointer, Yorkshire terrier, chihuahua.

9. What purpose is served by cats' whiskers? Should they be cut?

10. What is the average normal life expectancy of:
    (a) horses; (b) mice; (c) guinea-pigs?

11. What is the other name for a guinea-pig? Why is the name guinea-pig inappropriate?

12. What is the average normal gestation period (to within five days) of: (a) rabbits; (b) mice; (c) guinea-pigs?

PET ANIMALS

1. (*a*) 12–16 years;
   (*b*) 10–14 years;
   (*c*) 6–8 years.

2. Tabby, tortoise-shell and Siamese.

3. Finch and parrot.

4. (*a*) breed of dog originating in Russia;
   (*b*) small rodent.

5. When it is on a highway or in a public place.

6. 6 months.

7. (*a*) 61–63 days;
   (*b*) 62–65 days;
   (*c*) 336–337 days.

8. Mastiff and pointer are large dogs.

9. They are an important aid to their sense of touch. They should not be cut.

10. (*a*) 20–30 years;
    (*b*) 2 years;
    (*c*) 3 years.

11. Cavy. It does not originate from Guinea and it is not a pig.

12. (*a*) 31–32 days;
    (*b*) 18–20 days;
    (*c*) 68–70 days.

PHOTOGRAPHY

1. What name is given to a lens of shorter focal length and wider angle of view than a normal lens?

2. What name is given to a lens of longer focal length and narrower angle of view than a normal lens?

3. What is the 'focal length' of a lens?

4. What is 'depth of field' and what factors cause it to vary?

5. (a) How much faster is a film-speed rating of ASA 125 than a rating of ASA 64?
   (b) How much faster is a film-speed rating of DIN 24 than a rating of DIN 18?

6. What is the advantage of using an ultra-violet filter on a camera lens?

7. What is a 'zoom' lens?

8. Which of these cameras is *not* made in Japan?
   Minolta, Canon, Praktica, Nikon, Yashica.

9. What name is given to a film that is sensitive to all the colours of the spectrum?

10. What do the f numbers on a lens mean?

11. How much more light is admitted to a lens at an aperture of f 5.6 than one at f 11?

12. What is aperture-priority exposure and what is shutter-priority exposure?

PHOTOGRAPHY

1. Wide-angle.

2. Telephoto.

3. The distance between the centre of the lens and the point on the focal plane at which the image of a subject is sharply focused.

4. The range of distance within which objects retain their sharpness of focus. It varies with the size of aperture, distance of subject and focal length.

5. (*a*) twice;   (*b*) four times.

6. It reduces the haze in black-and-white photos and the bluishness in colour photos.

7. A lens of variable focal length. (It is easy to get a precise framing of the picture and eliminates the need for separate wide-angle and telephoto lenses.)

8. Praktica.

9. Panchromatic.

10. They indicate how much light the aperture allows through the lens. (An *f* number is the ratio of the aperture diameter to the focal length of the lens.)

11. Four times.

12. In the former the operator sets the desired aperture and the exposure meter sets the shutter speed. In the latter the operator sets the shutter speed.

PLAIN ENGLISH

Rewrite these sentences in plain and simple English.

1. That gives us a percentage of the overall figure.

2. The children number upwards of one hundred but there is a complete absence of the male sex.

3. An increase in the living units in the country would prove detrimental to the visual amenities.

4. The cessation of house-building operated during such time as Smith's chairmanship eventuated.

5. I will give consideration to the possibility of carrying into effect an ongoing dialogue.

6. He was the recipient of the majority of the abuse.

7. The availability of carpets is diminishing therefore I must ascertain the position of how many remain.

8. He does not see his way to actuating the event within the time-scale of any meaningful period.

9. It is desirable for them at this moment in time to attain unanimity on the dimensions of the project.

10. Only one additional item has been added so at the end of the day it remains much as formerly the case.

11. Has that equine quadruped an actual nomenclature?

12. With regard to the parameters of any contingency action we cannot foresee any escalation on our part.

PLAIN ENGLISH

1. That gives us some of the total.

2. There are more than a hundred children but no boys.

3. More houses in the country would be unsightly.

4. No houses were built while Smith was chairman.

5. I will think about having a continuous discussion.

6. He received most of the abuse.

7. Carpets are getting scarcer so I must see how many are left.

8. He will not do it in a definite time.

9. It is best for them now to agree on the size of the project.

10. Only one item has been added so finally it remains much as it was.

11. Has that horse got a name?

12. We will not extend the limits of any future action.

POST and TELEPHONE

1. What is the maximum weight limit for: (*a*) first-class letters; (*b*) second-class letters; (*c*) inland parcels?

2. How does a certificate of posting differ from a compensation fee certificate of posting?

3. Can first-class *and* second-class letters and packets be sent by registered post?

4. For how long is a postal order valid?

5. Within how many days after posting are the following normally delivered? (*a*) first-class letters; (*b*) second-class letters; (*c*) inland parcels.

6. Are letters and parcels from the United Kingdom to the Republic of Ireland charged at inland rates?

7. What number should you dial from abroad to call the UK telephone number 0638 2233?

8. Which telephone number should be dialled for:
   (*a*) emergencies; (*b*) operator; (*c*) directory enquiries?

9. Which is the more expensive telephone rental – private or business?

10. What have these in common? Explosive materials, obscene literature, counterfeit banknotes.

11. What is Datapost Sameday?

12. What does it cost to call a telephone number starting with the figures 0800 or with 0345?

POST and TELEPHONE

1. (*a*) no limit;
   (*b*) 750 grams;
   (*c*) 30 kilograms.

2. A certificate of posting is for letters and parcels; compensation up to a small fixed sum is payable. A compensation fee certificate of posting is for parcels; compensation up to a large sum is payable.

3. No, only first-class.

4. 6 months from the last day of the month of issue.

5. (*a*) 1 day;
   (*b*) 3 days;
   (*c*) 2 days.

6. No, at overseas rates.

7. The international code for the UK (which is not the same number from all countries) followed by 638 2233 (i.e. omit the 0 from 0638).

8. (*a*) 999;   (*b*) 100;   (*c*) 192 (London, 142).

9. Business.

10. They are included in the list of articles that may not be sent through the post.

11. Collection/delivery of goods/documents the same day.

12. 0800 – the call is free;
    0345 – the call is charged at local call rates.

PROPERTY and TAXES

1. On which of these is income tax payable?
   (*a*) building society interest;
   (*b*) National Savings Certificates interest;
   (*c*) unemployment benefit for husband and wife;
   (*d*) Premium Bonds winnings.

2. Is there a time limit for returning an income-tax return? What happens if you have not been sent one?

3. At what age can married couples claim age allowance?

4. Which of these are taxable? Gambling wins, education grants, tips, war-widow's pensions, widow's pensions.

5. Can one get tax relief on the interest paid on loans or mortgages for more than one house?

6. How can a deed of covenant help a charity?

7. If you start a business can you offset any early losses against the income when you were employed?

8. How is the number in a PAYE tax code calculated?

9. What is the name for a legal right over another person's land or property?

10. Which of these expenses can be offset against income from letting property? rates, repairs, wear and tear on furniture, insurance against loss of rent.

11. In how many ways does a motorist pay tax?

12. On which date does the tax year commence?

PROPERTY and TAXES

1. (*a*) (if you are a tax payer) and (*c*).

2. There is a time limit of 30 days for its return. If you have not been sent one it is your responsibility to notify the tax office of any changes.

3. When either of them reaches sixty-five, and a higher allowance when either of them reaches eighty.

4. Tips and widow's pensions.

5. No, tax relief is limited to the interest on a loan or mortgage to buy one's only or main home (normally the one lived in most of the time).

6. When a taxpayer makes a payment to a charity and deducts income tax from it the charity can reclaim the tax from the Inland Revenue. (The covenant must last for more than three years.)

7. Yes (within the relevant tax year).

8. The number is the total of your allowances with the last digit omitted. For example a person with allowances of £3210 would have a code number of 321.

9. Easement.

10. All except insurance against loss of rent.

11. A special car tax on the car's manufacture, VAT on the retail price, annual licence and petrol tax.

12. 6 April.

41. Questions

What do you READ?

1. Which of these are *daily* newspapers? *Observer, Financial Times, The Guardian, News of the World.*

2. What type of book would you expect by: (*a*) Barbara Cartland; (*b*) Delia Smith; (*c*) Jack Higgins?

3. Which of these famous books are fiction and which are fact? (*a*) *The Last Days of Pompeii;* (*b*) *Empire of the Sun;* (*c*) *Kon-Tiki;* (*d*) *Rural Rides.*

4. If a friend said that he was reading one of these authors which book would he probably mean? (*a*) Pepys; (*b*) Gibbon; (*c*) Chaucer; (*d*) Bunyan; (*e*) Cervantes.

5. What subjects would you expect to find in: (*a*) *Private Eye*; (*b*) *Lancet*; (*c*) *Choice*; (*d*) *Which?*

6. What is a *Baedeker* guide?

7. Which of these write detective novels? (*a*) P.D. James; (*b*) Susan Hill; (*c*) Ruth Rendell; (*d*) Iris Murdoch.

8. What subject would you associate with: (*a*) Desmond Morris; (*b*) Patrick Moore; (*c*) Michael Wood?

9. Who wrote: (*a*) *War and Peace;* (*b*) *The War of the Worlds?*

10. Name the *most* famous book by: (*a*) Jonathan Swift; (*b*) Daniel Defoe; (*c*) Henry Fielding; (*d*) Charlotte Brontë.

11. Name the four Gospels in correct Bible order.

12. In which of Shakespeare's plays would one find: (*a*) Polonius; (*b*) Touchstone; (*c*) Patience?

What do you READ?

1. The *Financial Times and The Guardian* are published daily, the *Observer* and *News of the World* on Sundays.

2. (*a*) romantic novel;
   (*b*) cookery;
   (*c*) thriller.

3. (*a*) and (*b*) are fiction;
   (*c*) and (*d*) are fact.

4. (*a*) *Diary of Samuel Pepys;*
   (*b*) *The History of the Decline and Fall of the Roman Empire;*
   (*c*) *The Canterbury Tales;*
   (*d*) *The Pilgrim's Progress;*
   (*e*) *Don Quixote.*

5. (*a*) satire;   (*b*) medicine;   (*c*) retirement;
   (*d*) consumer matters.

6. A travel guide to a country or city.

7. P.D. James and Ruth Rendell.

8. (*a*) anthropology;   (*b*) astronomy;   (*c*) archaeology.

9. (*a*) Tolstoy;   (*b*) H.G. Wells.

10. (*a*) *Gulliver's Travels;* (*b*) *Robinson Crusoe;*
    (*c*) *Tom Jones;* (*d*) *Jane Eyre.*

11. Matthew, Mark, Luke and John.

12. (*a*) *Hamlet;* (*b*) *As You Like It;* (*c*) *King Henry VIII.*

Using REFERENCE BOOKS

1. In which publication would you find:
   (*a*) last week's Parliamentary debates;
   (*b*) last month's world events;
   (*c*) last year's first-class cricket scores?

2. What information is contained in: (*a*) *The Statesman's Year Book;* (*b*) *The Annual Register?*

3. What is Roget's *Thesaurus?*

4. What information would you find in *Who's Who?*

5. Which series of books on England were edited and mainly compiled by: (*a*) Nikolaus Pevsner; (*b*) Arthur Mee?

6. Which famous reference books were compiled by:
   (*a*) John Bartlett; (*b*) E. Cobham Brewer; (*c*) Joseph Haydn?

7. Which standard book on English by Henry Fowler was first published in 1926?

8. On which subjects are these reference books?
   (*a*) *Halsbury;* (*b*) *Grove;* (*c*) *Hoyle.*

9. How many volumes are in a new set of: (*a*) *Dictionary of National Biography;* (*b*) *Encyclopaedia Britannica?*

10. Complete the following: (*a*) *Crockford's* . . . . . .
    (*b*) *The Victoria History of the* . . . . . .

11. Which is the odd one out of these? *Nagel, Baedeker, Fodor, Guinness, Blue Guide.*

12. What have Samuel Johnson and Noah Webster in common?

Using REFERENCE BOOKS

1. (*a*) *Hansard;*
   (*b*) *Keesing's Record of World Events;*
   (*c*) *Wisden Cricketer's Almanack.*

2. (*a*) statistics, descriptions and histories of all the countries of the world;
   (*b*) a record of world events in each year.

3. A book in which English words are grouped by ideas so that synonyms and associated words are found in appropriate groups.

4. Career details, honours, publications and hobbies of important living people.

5. (*a*) *The Buildings of England;*
   (*b*) *The King's England.*

6. (*a*) *Familiar Quotations;* (*b*) *Dictionary of Phrase and Fable;* (*c*) *Dictionary of Dates.*

7. *A Dictionary of Modern English Usage.*

8. (*a*) law;   (*b*) music;   (*c*) games.

9. (*a*) thirty (to 1980);   (*b*) thirty-two.

10. (*a*) *Clerical Directory;*
    (*b*) *Counties of England.*

11. *Guinness.* (The others are all travel guides.)

12. They both compiled famous dictionaries of the English language.

43. Questions

Rules of the ROAD

1. What is the legal minimum depth of tread on tyres fitted to motor cars?

2. What information must always be given to the other driver concerned in an accident?

3. When may a car be driven on the road without a test certificate?

4. If you hit and injure any of these animals must you report it? (*a*) dog; (*b*) cat; (*c*) cow; (*d*) pig.

5. Which of these is *not* a legal requirement on a motor car? speedometer, windscreen wipers, silencer, fog-lamp, rear-view mirror.

6. Within how many days must you produce your car documents if requested by the police?

7. (*a*) Are yellow headlamps legal?
(*b*) Are reversing lights compulsory?

8. What is the permitted maximum speed for cars on: (*a*) motorways; (*b*) dual carriageways; (*c*) other roads?

9. On which roads should headlamps be used?

10. Which of the exceptions to the requirement to wear a seat-belt when driving a car applies to everyone?

11. What is the shortest overall stopping distance of a car (to within 20 feet) at: (*a*) 50 m.p.h.; (*b*) 70 m.p.h?

12. Name two types of vehicle not allowed on motorways.

Rules of the ROAD

1. 1.6mm of tread throughout the central 75% of the tyre width and round the entire outer circumference.

2. Your name and address, the vehicle owner's name and address and the registration mark. (If anyone is injured the insurance certificate must be produced at the time or at a police station.)

3. If it is less than three years old, if it is being taken for a pre-arranged test to a testing station or taken home after a test, or if it is being tested by a garage during or after repairs to it.

4. (a) yes;   (b) no;   (c) yes;   (d) yes.

5. Fog-lamp.

6. Seven.

7. (a) yes, if the bulbs are yellow (masking is illegal); (b) no.

8. (a) 70 m.p.h.; (b) 70 m.p.h.; (c) 60 m.p.h.

9. Where there is no street lighting and where the street lamps are more than 200 yards apart.

10. When reversing.

11. (a) 175 feet;   (b) 315 feet.

12. Invalid carriages of 5 cwt. or less unladen, certain slow-moving vehicles, vehicles driven by learners, motor cycles under 50 c.c. and agricultural vehicles.

SAFETY

1. In a safety plug which colour wire goes into the live, neutral and earth terminal respectively?

2. Which of these should have 13-amp fuses in their plugs? steam iron, kettle, food-mixer, electric blanket, washing-machine, toaster.

3. Which one of these cleaning agents is *not* inflammable? acetone, bleach, white spirit, methylated spirit.

4. Which of these has the highest rate of injury? judo, rugby football, soccer, fencing, cricket.

5. Which of these types of accident is most frequent in the home? fire, suffocation, poisoning, falling.

6. Why is a pull-cord electric switch the safest type?

7. What should never be used to extinguish an oil or fat fire?

8. Which types of electrical appliance do *not* need earth conductors?

9. Which is the most burglar-proof type of door lock?

10. Which of these types of injury is most frequent in the home? cut, fracture, bruise, sprain, burn.

11. Which of these causes most fires in the home and why? gas fire, electric heater, cigarettes, chip pan.

12. Do most burglaries take place by day or by night? How old are most burglars?

SAFETY

1. Old colour code: red, black and green;
   new colour code: brown, blue, and green-and-yellow.

2. Kettle, washing-machine and toaster. (If over 720 watts a 13-amp fuse is needed.)

3. Bleach.

4. Rugby football.

5. Falling (about 50%).

6. Its use avoids the touching of a metal switch with wet hands, a common cause of electrocution.

7. Water – it will have an explosive effect. (Earth or sand should not be used either.)

8. Double-insulated appliances and non-metal light fittings.

9. Mortise deadlock. (One with five levers is the minimum security standard.)

10. Cut (about 34%). (Children suffer most from cuts, old people from fractures and dislocations.)

11. Chip pan (because fat ignites spontaneously when it reaches about 204° Centigrade).

12. Two-thirds of burglaries occur by day and about four-fifths when the house is empty. Two-thirds of burglars are teenagers. (Most burglars are opportunists and not professionals.)

SCIENTIFIC TERMS

1. Which one of these is *not* a unit of electrical measurement? ampere, joule, ohm, volt.

2. Name two of the three types of particle that are present in an atom.

3. What is the name for the quantity of heat required to raise the temperature of 1 gram of water by 1°Centigrade?

4. What is measured on these scales?
   (*a*) Richter; (*b*) Mohs; (*c*) Beaufort; (*d*) Réaumur.

5. What is an electrode? What are the names for the positive and negative electrodes?

6. What is a catalyst?

7. What are these sciences? (*a*) genetics; (*b*) cybernetics; (*c*) kinetics.

8. What are: (*a*) myopia; (*b*) presbyopia; (*c*) Daltonism?

9. Which of these geological periods came first? Palaeozoic, Mesozoic, Cainozoic,

10. What is a microchip?

11. In connection with computers what do the abbreviations ROM and RAM stand for?

12. Which word describes: (*a*) liquid that does not flow freely; (*b*) metal that can be shaped by hammering; (*c*) metal that can be drawn out into wire or thread?

SCIENTIFIC TERMS

1. Joule.

2. Electron, neutron and proton.

3. Calorie.

4. (*a*) earthquakes;   (*b*) hardness of minerals;
   (*c*) wind speeds;   (*d*) temperatures.

5. A solid conductor through which electricity enters or leaves a vacuum, battery or cell. The positive is the anode and the negative is the cathode.

6. A substance that facilitates a chemical change or reaction without itself undergoing any permanent change.

7. (*a*) heredity and variation in animals and plants;
   (*b*) control and communication mechanisms in animals and machines;
   (*c*) relations between the motions of bodies and the forces acting upon them.

8. (*a*) short-sightedness;   (*b*) long-sightedness;
   (*c*) colour-blindness.

9. Palaeozoic.

10. A tiny piece of silicon holding a complex electronic circuit.

11. Read-only memory and random-access memory.

12. (*a*) viscous;   (*b*) malleable;   (*c*) ductile.

SHOPPING RIGHTS

1. If you attend a neighbour's party where goods are for sale do you have the usual consumer protection?

2. If an article is lost or damaged while awaiting repair in a shop is the shopkeeper responsible?

3. If you receive unsolicited goods by post may you keep them without paying for them?

4. Is a shopkeeper obliged to give you change?

5. If goods are not delivered by the promised date of delivery can you cancel your order?

6. Where in a restaurant must the prices be displayed?

7. Is a shop bound to sell you goods at the price that is marked on them?

8. Does a notice 'No refunds on sale goods' have any legal force?

9. If you return an article with a serious defect to a shop to which of these are you legally entitled?
   refund or damages, replacement, credit note.

10. When can you refuse to pay a restaurant service charge?

11. Is a shopkeeper obliged to sell you an article that is displayed for sale?

12. If you innocently buy stolen goods can you get your money back? What happens to the goods?

SHOPPING RIGHTS

1. Yes, you are covered by the Sale of Goods Act 1979 and a Code of Practice for private parties.

2. Yes, unless he can prove that he was *not* negligent. (Displaying a notice disclaiming responsibility does not have any legal effect.)

3. Yes, if they have not been collected within six months (or thirty days if you have sent a letter to the owners asking them to collect the goods).

4. No, legally you should pay the correct amount.

5. Yes (but only if a definite date was stated in writing at the time of ordering).

6. A customer must be able to read a menu or price-list in a restaurant or public house before sitting down.

7. No. (The marked price might be a genuine mistake.)

8. No, goods in a sale are no different from other goods.

9. You are legally entitled to a refund or damages but not to a replacement or a credit note.

10. When there is no indication on the menu or price-list that a service charge is in operation.

11. No, he can refuse to sell without giving any reason.

12. To get your money back you would have to sue the seller of the goods. In most cases the goods must be returned to their rightful owner.

SIGHTS in the BRITISH ISLES

1. Where and what are: (*a*) The Needles; (*b*) Cleopatra's Needle?

2. Where are the birthplaces of: (*a*) Winston Churchill; (*b*)Gladstone; (*c*) Queen Victoria: (*d*) Duke of Wellington?

3. Where are the graves of the above?

4. Where and what are: (*a*) Malham Cove: (*b*) Lulworth Cove?

5. Where are these bridges and which rivers to they cross? (*a*) Royal Albert;   (*b*) Royal Border.

6. Which island off the English coast is accessible by car only at low tide?

7. Where can these ships be seen? (*a*) SS *Great Britain;* (*b*) HMS *Victory*.

8. Which type of bridge can be seen in the British Isles only at Newport and Middlesbrough?

9. Where can one see these? (*a*) Furry Dance; (*b*) Tynwald Ceremony; (*c*) Up-Helly-Aa'; (*d*) Flitch Trial.

10. Where are these? (*a*) Shakespeare Memorial Theatre; (*b*) Royal Liver Building; (*c*) Royal Pavilion.

11. If you were at Land's End, Lizard Point or Lowestoft Ness where could you claim to be respectively?

12. What happens at: (*a*) Ashbourne, Derbyshire, at Shrovetide; (*b*) Padstow, Cornwall, on 1 May; (*c*) Olney, Bucks., on Shrove Tuesday; (*d*) Henley-on-Thames in early June?

SIGHTS in the BRITISH ISLES

1. (*a*) isolated chalk masses off the south-west tip of the Isle of Wight; (*b*) an Egyptian obelisk at Victoria Embankment, London.

2. (*a*) Blenheim Palace;   (*b*) Liverpool;
   (*c*) Kensington Palace; (*d*) Dublin.

3. (*a*) Bladon, Oxfordshire;   (*b*) Westminster Abbey;
   (*c*) Frogmore, Windsor;   (*d*) St Paul's Cathedral.

4. (*a*) a high limestone cliff at Malham, North Yorkshire;
   (*b*) an almost land-locked bay in Dorset.

5. (*a*) the Tamar between Plymouth and Saltash;
   (*b*) the Tweed at Berwick-upon-Tweed.

6. Lindisfarne (Holy Island).

7. (*a*) Great Western Dock, Bristol; (*b*) Her Majesty's Naval Base, Portsmouth.

8. Transporter.

9. (*a*) Helston, Cornwall;   (*b*) St John's, Isle of Man;
   (*c*) Lerwick, Shetland;   (*d*) Great Dunmow, Essex.

10. (*a*) Stratford-upon-Avon;   (*b*) Liverpool;   (*c*) Brighton.

11. At the westernmost, southernmost and easternmost points of England.

12. (*a*) a game of football on a two-mile-long 'pitch';
    (*b*) a 'hobby-horse' parade; (*c*) a pancake race;
    (*d*) the Royal Regatta.

SIMPLE SCIENCE

1. Is water a good or a poor conductor of:
   (*a*) electricity;   (*b*) heat;   (*c*) sound?

2. Why can a needle float on water, and small insects walk on water?

3. On how many days in the year does a sundial agree with the clock, allowing for British Summer Time?
   1   4   13   30   52   365

4. Is air warmed by the direct rays of the sun?

5. Give the seven colours of the spectrum in their correct order.

6. Why is a thick drinking-glass more likely to crack than a thin glass when hot water is poured into it?

7. How does one convert degrees Fahrenheit to degrees Centigrade and vice versa?

8. Which *meter* would you use to find the:
   (*a*) density of milk; (*b*) density of a liquid;
   (*c*) humidity of the atmosphere; (*d*) diameter of a wire?

9. Why are there spaces between the ends of some adjoining rails in a railway track?

10. Which is the hardest of all known substances?

11. What is the main advantage of Polaroid lenses?

12. What is the boiling point of water in degrees Fahrenheit and degrees Centigrade?

SIMPLE SCIENCE

1. (*a*) good;   (*b*) poor;   (*c*) good.

2. Because of surface tension, an invisible skin or surface layer of water molecules.

3. Four: 15 April, 15 June, 1 September and 24 December.

4. No, by heat from the earth's surface.

5. Red, orange, yellow, green, blue, indigo, violet.

6. Glass is a poor conductor of heat, so the inside of the drinking-glass expands more quickly than the outside and this uneven expansion causes the glass to crack.

7. To convert Fahrenheit to Centigrade deduct 32 and multiply by 5/9; to convert Centigrade to Fahrenheit multiply by 9/5 and add 32.

8. (*a*) lactometer;
   (*b*) hydrometer;
   (*c*) hygrometer;
   (*d*) micrometer.

9. To allow for expansion of the metal rails in very hot weather.

10. Diamond.

11. They eliminate most of the reflected glare without too much general darkening.

12. 212° Fahrenheit and 100° Centigrade.

The rules of SOCCER

1. Can a goal be scored: (*a*) direct from a corner; (*b*) from a direct free kick; (*c*) direct from a throw-in; (*d*) direct from a kick-off; (*e*) by a goalkeeper?

2. (*a*) If a player hits the goal-post from a penalty kick can he score a goal from the rebound? (*b*) If the ball rebounds from the goalkeeper can he score?

3. (*a*) How far from the ball must defenders stand when a free kick is taken? (*b*) How many steps may a goal-keeper take while carrying the ball?

4. When is a player offside?

5. How far is the penalty spot from the goal-line?

6. For what two reasons must a referee extend the 45 minutes playing time of either half?

7. (*a*) How many substitutes is a team allowed in a League or FA Cup match? (*b*) When may a player be substituted?

8. How far apart are the goal-posts and how high is the crossbar?

9. May a goalkeeper move while a penalty is taken?

10. May a player come on or leave the field without the referee's permission?

11. What is the penalty for: (*a*) being offside; (*b*) pushing an opponent?

12. What does the arc outside the penalty area indicate?

The rules of SOCCER

1. (*a*) yes;   (*b*) yes;   (*c*) no;   (*d*) no;   (*e*) yes.

2. (*a*) no, but another player can;   (*b*) yes.

3. (*a*) 10 yards;   (*b*) four.

4. When he is nearer his opponents' goal-line than the ball at the moment the ball is played, unless he is in his own half of the field, or there are two opponents nearer to their own goal-line than he is, or the ball was last played by an opponent, or he receives it from a goal kick, corner or throw-in or after being dropped by the referee.

5. 12 yards.

6. To make up time lost by injuries and to enable a penalty kick to be taken.

7. (*a*) two;
   (*b*) at any time.

8. 8 yards and 8 feet respectively.

9. He may move his arms but not his legs.

10. No.

11. (*a*) indirect free kick (if interfering with the play or with an opponent); (*b*) direct free kick.

12. Every point on the arc is 10 yards from the penalty spot so that players can keep the required distance from the ball when a penalty kick is taken.

How do you SPELL it?

Three words in each of these groups of six are spelt incorrectly. Give the correct spelling of each word.

1. accessory, accomodation, ancilliary, artefact, conscientious, dessicated.

2. cattarrh, besiege, conjuror, glueing, guage, ecstasy.

3. derivitive, disappointed, definetive, dissipated, disassociate, eisteddfod.

4. benifited, gramaphone, hypocrisy, haemorrhage, irresistable, idiosyncrasy.

5. frieze, hygeine, liquify, received, pyjamas, marshall.

6. harassment, inoculate, instalment, mantlepiece, meridien, millenium.

7. insistence, mischievous, miniscule, perserverance, percolator, numbskull.

8. narcisus, pallette, redundent, sheriff, subtly, thieves.

9. plenitude, occurence, recommend, paralell, sanitorium, symbolism.

10. intergration, formatted, sacreligious, embarass, titillate, transitory.

11. putrefy, rarified, rythm, seperate, threshold, worship.

12. supercede, unequivocal, unconscious, vaccillate, vahement, vermilion.

How do you SPELL it?

1. accommodation, ancillary, desiccated.
2. catarrh, gluing, gauge.
3. derivative, definitive, dissociate.
4. benefited, gramophone, irresistible.
5. hygiene, liquefy, marshal.
6. mantelpiece, meridian, millennium.
7. minuscule, perseverance, numskull.
8. narcissus, palette, redundant.
9. occurrence, parallel, sanatorium.
10. integration, sacrilegious, embarrass.
11. rarefied, rhythm, separate.
12. supersede, vacillate, vehement.

The rules of SPORTS

1. What is the maximum number of clubs that each player may use in a round of golf?

2. In Rugby football in which direction may the ball be: (*a*) kicked; (*b*) thrown?

3. What is a tie-break in tennis? How is it scored?

4. How many players make a team in: (*a*) hockey; (*b*) ice hockey; (*c*) polo; (*d*) water polo; (*e*) Rugby League football; (*f*) Rugby Union football?

5. What is the difference between match-play and stroke-play in golf?

6. How are points scored in outdoor bowls?

7. How many players make a team in: (*a*) volleyball; (*b*) basketball; (*c*) netball; (*d*) rounders; (*e*) hurling; (*f*) baseball?

8. How long is the playing time in: (*a*) hockey; (*b*) ice hockey; (*c*) Rugby football?

9. In hockey is there a penalty for raising the stick above the shoulder?

10. How are points awarded in professional boxing?

11. How many points are awarded for tries and goals in Rugby Union and Rugby League football respectively?

12. (*a*) What age must horses be in the five classic races? (*b*) Which two races are for fillies only?

The rules of SPORTS

1. Fourteen.

2. (*a*) any direction;   (*b*) any direction except forwards.

3. A tie-break is played when the score is six-all in any set (except usually the final set). The winner is the first to score seven points with a lead of two points; at six-all the game continues until the lead is two points.

4. (*a*) 11;   (*b*) 6;   (*c*) 4;   (*d*) 7;   (*e*) 13;   (*f*) 15.

5. In match-play the winner is the player or side that wins most holes. In stroke-play the winner is the one that takes fewest strokes over the course.

6. Each wood nearer to the jack than any opposing wood scores one point.

7. (*a*) 6;   (*b*) 5;   (*c*) 7;   (*d*) 9;   (*e*) 15;   (*f*) 9.

8. (*a*) 70 minutes;   (*b*) 60 minutes;   (*c*) 80 minutes.

9. Yes.

10. A maximum number of points is awarded to the better boxer in each round and a proportionate number to the other boxer, or if equal the maximum to each.

11. Rugby Union: try – four; goal from a try – two; goal from a penalty or a free kick or a dropped goal – three. Rugby League: try – three; goal – two.

12. (*a*) three years old;
    (*b*) the Oaks and the One Thousand Guineas.

SUN, MOON and STARS

1. How many minutes later or earlier is sunrise or sunset for each degree of longitude?

2. How can you find due north by observing the stars?

3. How can you find your direction by using your watch and the sun?

4. Which phase of the moon is always in the opposite part of the sky to the sun?

5. Which five planets can be seen with the naked eye?

6. Why is the sky blue?

7. Why do we always see the same side of the moon?

8. (a) Excluding the sun and the moon which is the brightest object in the sky?
   (b) Which is the brightest star in the sky?

9. How many stars are visible to the naked eye on a clear night at any one moment?
   1000–1200, 2000–2500, 5000–6000, over 10,000.

10. How long does light from the sun and moon respectively take to reach the earth?
    1 second, 10 seconds, 2 minutes, $8\frac{1}{2}$ minutes, 4 hours.

11. How long does light from the nearest star take to reach the earth? 4 hours, 24 hours, 6 days, 4 years.

12. Why can we see the moon when it is actually below the horizon (i.e. before rising or after setting)?

SUN, MOON and STARS

1. 4 minutes.

2. Look for the Plough, a group of seven stars in the Great Bear constellation. An imaginary line joining the last two, when extended, points to the Pole Star, which is directly above the North Pole.

3. Point the hour hand at the sun. Note the angle the hour hand makes with the 12 and bisect it. The line bisecting the angle is due south. (In British Summer Time turn the hour hand back one hour first.)

4. Full moon.

5. Mercury, Venus, Mars, Saturn and Jupiter.

6. The sun's rays are scattered by water-vapour and dust when passing through the atmosphere; the blue rays are scattered the most so the sky appears blue.

7. Because it rotates on its axis in the same time (about 4 weeks) that it revolves about the earth.

8. (*a*) Venus;   (*b*) Sirius.

9. 2000–2500.

10. The moon – 1 second; the sun – $8\frac{1}{2}$ minutes.

11. 4 years.

12. Because light rays from the moon are refracted by the atmosphere by about half a degree, which as it happens is also the apparent diameter of the moon.

TRAVELLING in or from the U.K.

1. Is it illegal to share the costs of your regular car journeys by accepting payments from passengers?

2. If all second-class seats on a train are occupied are you allowed to sit in a first-class seat?

3. Name the three major airports that serve London.

4. What and how much should one drink on a long flight?

5. From which London railway station would one travel to:
(*a*) Edinburgh; (*b*) Norwich; (*c*) Bristol; (*d*) Manchester?

6. Which cities are served by airports at:
(*a*) Dyce; (*b*) Speke; (*c*) Eastleigh; (*d*) Elmdon?

7. For how many years are these valid? (*a*) British standard passport; (*b*) British visitor's passport.

8. Which cathedral city lies between:
(*a*) Monmouth and Ludlow; (*b*) Cambridge and King's Lynn; (*c*) Tamworth and Stafford; (*d*) Southampton and Newbury?

9. Which two towns in Great Britain are furthest apart by rail?

10. In which counties are these towns?
(*a*) Ludlow; (*b*) Thetford; (*c*) Rye; (*d*) Penrith.

11. Which of these cities are situated close to the M1 motorway? Leicester, Coventry, Nottingham, Sheffield.

12. Name two ferry ports that serve the Isle of Wight.

TRAVELLING in or from the U.K.

1. No (provided that you do not make a profit).

2. Not without the permission of a guard or inspector. (A ticket does not entitle you to a seat.)

3. Heathrow, Gatwick and Stansted.

4. Plenty of water or fruit squash (not alcohol) – up to 5 pints in 24 hours.

5. (*a*) King's Cross;
   (*b*) Liverpool Street;
   (*c*) Paddington;
   (*d*) Euston.

6. (*a*) Aberdeen;   (*b*) Liverpool;
   (*c*) Southampton;   (*d*) Birmingham.

7. (*a*) 10 years (5 years if under sixteen); (*b*) 1 year.

8. (*a*) Hereford;   (*b*) Ely;
   (*c*) Lichfield;   (*d*) Winchester.

9. Penzance (Cornwall) and Wick (Highland).

10. (*a*) Shropshire;
    (*b*) Norfolk;
    (*c*) East Sussex;
    (*d*) Cumbria.

11. Leicester, Nottingham and Sheffield.

12. Lymington, Portsmouth and Southampton.

Is it TRUE?

1. (*a*) Is a spider an insect?   (*b*) Is a firefly a fly?
   (*c*) Is a whale a fish?   (*d*) Is a reindeer a deer?

2. Is ozone found at the seaside? Is it good for you?

3. (*a*) Does a lead pencil contain lead?
   (*b*) Is rice-paper made from rice?

4. (*a*) Was Queen Cleopatra an Egyptian?
   (*b*) Was Catherine the Great a Russian?

5. Why is it wrong to say that a bride walked down the aisle?

6. What is the name of the Cathedral of Rome?

7. (*a*) Who invented the piston steam-engine?
   (*b*) Who first flew the Atlantic non-stop?
   (*c*) Who invented the telescope?

8. Who was the first man to circumnavigate the world?

9. When sailing through the Panama Canal from the Atlantic to the Pacific in which direction would one be travelling?

10. Did Nero fiddle while Rome burned?

11. Correct this quotation: 'Alas, poor Yorick! I knew him well.'

12. (*a*) Does a red rag incite a bull?
    (*b*) Do bees gather honey?
    (*c*) Does a centipede have a hundred legs?

Is it TRUE?

1. (*a*) no, an arachnid;
   (*b*) no, a beetle;
   (*c*) no, a mammal;
   (*d*) yes.

2. Ozone occurs in the atmosphere mainly at altitudes above 20 kilometres, and near the earth in such minute quantities that it has no effect on humans.

3. (*a*) no, the 'lead' in a pencil is mainly graphite;
   (*b*) no, it is made from the pith of an Asiatic tree.

4. (*a*) no, she was part Greek, part Macedonian;
   (*b*) no, she was born in Prussia.

5. The aisles of a church nave are at the side, not in the middle.

6. St John Lateran (*not* St Peter's).

7. (*a*) Thomas Newcomen (*not* James Watt);
   (*b*) Alcock and Whitten-Brown (*not* Lindbergh);
   (*c*) Hans Lippershey (*not* Galileo).

8. Sebastian del Cano (*not* Ferdinand Magellan).

9. From north-west to south-east.

10. No, the violin was invented in the sixteenth century.

11. It should be 'Alas, poor Yorick! I knew him, Horatio:'.

12. (*a*) no, bulls are colour-blind; (*b*) no, they gather nectar;
    (*c*) no, common ones have about thirty legs.

WEIGHTS and MEASURES

1. If you buy 36 litres of petrol for your car how many gallons is that?

2. Your house and garden cover 15,000 square metres. How large is that in terms of acreage?

3. The upper weight limit for parcels at some post offices is 10 kilograms. What is that in pounds?

4. The temperature today is 28° Centigrade. What is that on the Fahrenheit scale? Yesterday it was 65° Fahrenheit. What is that on the Centigrade scale?

5. At what temperature do the Centigrade and Fahrenheit scales coincide?

6. (a) The distance between A and B is 322 kilometres. How many miles is that? (b) The distance between B and C is 100 miles. How many kilometres is that?

7. Your car travels 10 kilometres on 1 litre of petrol. How many miles per gallon is that?

8. How long is a: (a) cricket pitch; (b) tennis court; (c) nautical mile; (d) fathom?

9. What is a: (a) hectare; (b) decimetre?

10. How much does 10 gallons of water weigh in pounds?

11. How much does 2 cubic feet of water weigh in pounds?

12. What is measured or weighed in:
    (a) carats; (b) crans; (c) cords?

WEIGHTS and MEASURES

1. 8 (7.92 more exactly).
   (1 gallon = 4.546 litres.)

2. About 3.7 acres.
   (1 square metre = 1.196 square yards and 4840 square yards = 1 acre.)

3. 22 (22.046 more exactly).

4. 28° Centigrade = 82.4° Fahrenheit.
   65° Fahrenheit = 18.3° Centigrade.

5. Minus 40 degrees.

6. (a) about 200; (b) about 160. (1 mile = 1.609 kilometres, and 1 kilometre = 0.621 miles.)

7. Approximately 28.25.

8. (a) 22 yards;
   (b) 26 yards;
   (c) 6080 feet;
   (d) 6 feet.

9. (a) 10,000 square metres;
   (b) one-tenth of a metre.

10. About 100 pounds.

11. About 125 pounds.

12. (a) diamonds and precious stones, and also the fineness of gold; (b) herrings; (c) usually wood, and also sometimes stone.

WILD ANIMALS

1. Which is the smallest British flesh-eating mammal?

2. Which of these birds may be shot because they are regarded as a nuisance? magpie, jay, robin, rook, owl, starling, blackbird, jackdaw.

3. Where would you find the nests of these birds?
   (*a*) kingfisher; (*b*) house-martin; (*c*) goldcrest; (*d*) cuckoo.

4. (*a*) Are bats blind? (*b*) What do they mostly eat?
   (*c*) Which is the commonest type of British bat?

5. Which of these are summer migrants to Great Britain? lapwing, swift, swallow, woodpecker, cuckoo, kingfisher.

6. What is the main food of: (*a*) foxes; (*b*) otters; (*c*) owls; (*d*) hedgehogs?

7. What is the main difference in appearance between frogs and toads?

8. Name two of the seven species of deer in Great Britain. Name one of the two native species.

9. Which of these may you kill at *any* time of the year? rabbits, deer, game birds, foxes, freshwater fish.

10. Which of these are freshwater fish? bass, sturgeon, grayling, whiting, pike, tench, plaice, roach, carp.

11. Which is the smallest and which is the largest British wild animal?

12. Which root-eater is Great Britain's largest rodent?

WILD ANIMALS

1. Weasel.

2. Magpie, jay, rook, starling and jackdaw.

3. (a) a hole in a river-bank;
   (b) under the eaves of a house;
   (c) usually hanging from a branch of a conifer;
   (d) it uses the nests of other birds.

4. (a) they have poor eyesight but are not blind;
   (b) insects (they hunt by emitting high-pitched sounds that are reflected back from their prey);
   (c) pipistrelle.

5. Swift, swallow and cuckoo.

6. (a) small animals (rabbits, rats, squirrels, frogs, birds);
   (b) fish (especially eels, salmon, trout);
   (c) mice, voles and shrews;
   (d) insects, snails, slugs, worms and beetles.

7. Frogs have soft, smooth, moist skins and toads have tough, thick, dry skins and shorter limbs.

8. Roe-deer, red deer, fallow deer, reindeer, sika, muntjac and Chinese water-deer. The first two are natives.

9. Rabbits and foxes.

10. Grayling, pike, tench, roach and carp.

11. Pygmy shrew and red deer.

12. Coypu.

WINES and SPIRITS

1. What two tests can be made by *looking* at a wine?

2. Which three countries in Europe are the largest producers of wine?

3. What is the main reason for decanting red wine?

4. What is a fortified wine?

5. From which countries do these wines originate?
   (*a*) Chianti;   (*b*) liebfraumilch;
   (*c*) port;   (*d*) muscadet.

6. Which factors should be taken into account when one selects a storage place for wines?

7. Why are most wines stored horizontally?

8. Name the following:
   (*a*) spirit made from molasses or sugar cane;
   (*b*) Japanese fermented liquor made from rice;
   (*c*) dark, heavy ale with a pronounced taste of malt;
   (*d*) green or yellow liqueur made by Carthusian monks.

9. Is red wine best with meat and white wine with fish, or vice versa?

10. What type of wine is: (*a*) St-Émilion; (*b*) Asti spumante?

11. What are the basic ingredients of a:
    (*a*) Manhattan cocktail;   (*b*) dry Martini?

12. Beers and wines contain what percentage of alcohol respectively?

WINES and SPIRITS

1. Its clarity, by holding it up to the light, and its colour, by looking through it with a white background.

2. Italy, France and Spain.

3. To clear the wine of sediment.

4. One that has been made stronger by the addition of alcohol or brandy during or after fermentation.

5. (*a*) Italy; (*b*) Germany; (*c*) Portugal; (*d*) France.

6. It should have an even temperature, darkness, no vibration, no smell, and be not too damp or too dry.

7. To keep the cork in contact with the wine so that it does not shrink and admit air to the bottle.

8. (*a*) rum;
   (*b*) saki or saké;
   (*c*) stout;
   (*d*) chartreuse.

9. With a few exceptions, such as salmon, red with meat and white with fish.

10. (*a*) red wine from Bordeaux;
    (*b*) sparkling sweet white wine from Piedmont.

11. (*a*) two parts rye whiskey, one part vermouth and a dash of bitters; (*b*) four parts gin, one part vermouth.

12. Beers 3–7 per cent; wines 8–20 per cent.

There is a WORD for it

1. Give the word for the apparent movement of an object caused by the change in position of the observer.

2. What is the word for the study of:
   (*a*) birds; (*b*) poisons; (*c*) fishes; (*d*) reptiles?

3. A mania is a compulsive desire for something. Which mania is a desire for: (*a*) books; (*b*) alcohol?

4. What is the word for a principle or standard by which something is judged?

5. What is the word for a: (*a*) tomb named after a king of Caria; (*b*) type of hat named after a Victorian novel?

6. Give the word for a hater of: (*a*) women; (*b*) mankind.

7. What do we call a word that means: (*a*) the same as a given word; (*b*) the opposite of a given word?

8. What is the word for a group of: (*a*) gulls; (*b*) crows; (*c*) nightingales; (*d*) squirrels; (*e*) lions; (*f*) rooks?

9. What is the word for a: (*a*) nonsense verse named after an Irish city; (*b*) jacket named after a famous earl?

10. What is the word for a model of supreme excellence?

11. What is the word used to describe something that: (*a*) can be seen through; (*b*) cannot be seen through?

12. Name the figure of speech in which: (*a*) one thing is compared with another; (*b*) a name or description is given to an object when not literally applicable.

There is a WORD for it

1. Parallax.

2. (*a*) ornithology;
   (*b*) toxicology;
   (*c*) ichthyology;
   (*d*) herpetology.

3. (*a*) bibliomania;
   (*b*) dipsomania.

4. Criterion.

5. (*a*) mausoleum;
   (*b*) trilby.

6. (*a*) misogynist;
   (*b*) misanthrope.

7. (*a*) synonym;
   (*b*) antonym.

8. (*a*) colony;   (*b*) murder;
   (*c*) watch;   (*d*) dray;
   (*e*) pride;   (*f*) building.

9. (*a*) limerick;
   (*b*) cardigan.

10. Paragon.

11. (*a*) transparent;
    (*b*) opaque.

12. (*a*) simile;   (*b*) metaphor.

What does that WORD mean?

1. These words are frequently seen. What do they mean?
   (*a*) salutary; (*b*) chronic; (*c*) viable; (*d*) lethargic.

2. What are the meanings of these 'isms'?
   (*a*) solecism; (*b*) euphemism; (*c*) plagiarism; (*d*) aphorism.

3. What are these branches of study? (*a*) entomology;
   (*b*) etymology; (*c*) philology; (*d*) speleology.

4. What do these 'meters' measure? (*a*) ammeter;
   (*b*) barometer; (*c*) pedometer; (*d*) chronometer.

5. Cruciform means 'shaped like a cross'. To which shapes
   do these words refer?
   (*a*) nuciform; (*b*) penniform; (*c*) cuneiform; (*d*) scutiform.

6. What are pyrotechnics?

7. To which animals do these adjectives apply?
   (*a*) lupine; (*b*) vulpine; (*c*) cervine; (*d*) ovine.

8. What is the difference between a panacea, a placebo
   and a plethora?

9. What is: (*a*) gibberish; (*b*) gobbledegook?

10. A 'phobia' is a fear of something. To what do these
    'phobias' refer? (*a*) agoraphobia; (*b*) claustrophobia;
    (*c*) xenophobia; (*d*) nyctophobia.

11. What is the meaning of: (*a*) flammable; (*b*) inflammable?

12. What is the difference between a Regius professor
    and an emeritus professor?

What does that WORD mean?

1. (*a*) producing good effects; (*b*) constantly present, long-lasting; (*c*) feasible, able to live; (*d*) lacking energy.

2. (*a*) offence against grammar, idiom or etiquette;
   (*b*) use of mild words for blunt ones;
   (*c*) use of someone's writings as one's own;
   (*d*) maxim or pithy saying.

3. (*a*) insects;   (*b*) derivation of words;
   (*c*) languages;   (*d*) caves.

4. (*a*) electric current; (*b*) atmospheric pressure; (*c*) distance or steps walked; (*d*) time.

5. (*a*) nut;   (*b*) feather;   (*c*) wedge;   (*d*) shield.

6. The making or displaying of fireworks.

7. (*a*) wolves;   (*b*) foxes;   (*c*) deer;   (*d*) sheep.

8. A panacea is a universal remedy, a placebo is a medicine given to please rather than to cure, and a plethora is an excess of anything.

9. (*a*) unintelligible speech; (*b*) pompous official jargon.

10. (*a*) open places; (*b*) enclosed places; (*c*) foreigners or strangers; (*d*) darkness or night.

11. (*a*) easily set on fire;   (*b*) easily set on fire!

12. A Regius professor is one appointed by royal mandate and an emeritus professor is one who has retired from office and holds an honorary title.

60. Questions

What would YOU do?

1. How should you stop water pouring through a ceiling from a burst or broken pipe?

2. What is the first thing to do when someone has had a shock from an electric appliance?

3. What is the most important thing to do if you are first on the scene of a serious road accident?

4. What are the next most important things to do?

5. What should you do if you are chased by a bull?

6. What should you do if you are caught in a lightning storm: (a) in the open; (b) under trees?

7. What should you do if your passport is lost abroad?

8. What is the first thing to do if you lose your credit card or cheque card?

9. If you are stuck in a snow-bound car should you:
   (a) run the heater as long as possible;
   (b) go in search of help;
   (c) keep windows tightly closed;
   (d) keep awake at all costs?

10. What should you do if your bank account is wrongly credited with £50?

11. What is the best way to unfreeze your car door locks?

12. What should you do if trapped in a quicksand?

What would YOU do?

1. Turn off the main stop tap to cut off the supply of cold water and open all the taps in the house to drain the cold water tank.

2. Switch off the current at the socket or pull out the plug – do not use the switch on the appliance.

3. Protect the area from oncoming traffic by hazard lights and warning triangles.

4. Send for the police, immobilise the vehicles involved and help the injured.

5. Try to reach a wall or fence while dodging the bull, but never turn your back on him.

6. (a) lie flat;
   (b) sit on something dry and if possible avoid contact with the ground, but do not climb a tree.

7. Report the loss to the local police and ask the nearest British consulate or embassy for a temporary passport to get you home.

8. Inform the credit card company or bank immediately.

9. (a) no;   (b) no;   (c) no;   (d) yes.

10. Tell the bank that they have made a mistake.

11. Heat the key or use an aerosol lock de-icer.

12. Lie on your back with arms outstretched and try to ease yourself out very slowly.